Sue Limb read English at Cambridge. Following an early
career as a teacher, she became a free-lance journalist and
then a writer and broadcaster. She is the author of several
radio scripts including *The Wordsmiths at Gorsemere*. She
co-authored a biography of Captain Oates before turning her
hand to fiction: *Up the Garden Path* was published to critical
acclaim in 1984. She is married to the composer Jan Vriend
and lives in Gloucestershire.

A belated present!

with love from

Alison, David

and Fiona

Also by Sue Limb

UP THE GARDEN PATH
LOVE'S LABOURS

and published by Corgi Books

THE WORDSMITHS AT GORSEMERE

published by Bantam Press

LOVE FORTY

Sue Limb

Illustrations by Chris Riddell

CORGI BOOKS

LOVE FORTY

A CORGI BOOK   0 552 12865 1

Originally published in Great Britain by
Bantam press, a division of Transworld Publishers Ltd.

PRINTING HISTORY
Bantam Press edition published 1986
Corgi edition published 1988
Corgi edition reprinted 1989
Corgi edition reprinted 1990

This book is set in 10/11pt Ballardvale

Corgi Books are published by Transworld Publishers Ltd.,
61–63 Uxbridge Road, Ealing, London W5 5SA,
in Australia by Transworld Publishers (Australia) Pty. Ltd.,
15–23 Helles Avenue, Moorebank, NSW 2170, and in New
Zealand by Transworld Publishers (N.Z.) Ltd., Cnr. Moselle
and Waipareira Avenues, Henderson, Auckland.

Reproduced, printed and bound in Great Britain by
BPCC Hazell Books
Aylesbury, Bucks, England
Member of BPCC Ltd.

For my parents

Chapter 1

It was Christmas Eve. A vast black night was unfolding around us, and we were headed west: beyond the tomato-soup glow of London's city lights, beyond graffiti, beyond beyond. We were already at Chiswick – seriously far west. I admit I was nervous. I was biting my fingernails right up to the armpit. It was partly the shock of leaving London (the worst shock, incidentally, since being born – and I'd been three weeks late with stage fright for that). Yes, dear womb-like London! Warm, noisy, lots of underground action, delicious foods reaching you through tubes, a sense of being at the solar plexus of the organism. Who could contemplate leaving all that without a qualm?

And then, the means of transport: a hired van of, I'm sorry to say, the very cheapest sort. Rattling about in the back were the bits of furniture I couldn't bear to part with – mostly wickerwork chairs which collapsed when you sat on them and creaked spookily when you didn't. Driving the van was a foreigner with whom, it seemed, I had thrown in some kind of lot. He hadn't driven for ten years and even then it had been abroad, which doesn't count.

'GIVE WAY!' I screeched as he accelerated towards another roundabout. I don't like to think what we nearly lost on those roundabouts. Mind you, I admit I'm the worst passenger in Western Europe. Anything over 10 m.p.h. and I close my eyes and offer my soul up to the Almighty. On this particular Christmas Eve my feet were firmly planted on the dashboard to act as shock absorbers and the nails that weren't being bitten to the quick were clinging on for grim death. And it would be a pretty grim death, wouldn't it: plastered all over one of those motorways west of London? I can't think of anything worse, except, perhaps, choking to death in a very quiet and classy New York restaurant.

'WATCH OUT – STOP!!' I shrieked. 'You may well say Watch Out and Stop to him, dear,' whispered my City Slicker Self, perturbed at our departure, 'but it wouldn't have been such a bad idea if you'd said it to yourself some time ago. Leaving London in a 1950s Rolls-Royce wouldn't be so bad, especially if we were headed for a house-party in a snug little village somewhere not too wild. But leaving in a hired van! And for – where was it again? South Wales? Well, frankly, you have seriously goofed here. This is not exactly the Christmas I had in mind. Not after last year.'

The Country Bumpkin in me twitched and rose to the defence of Westward Ho! 'There's choirs in the hills,' it mused. 'Wales is full of music. Lots of space, too. Fields and stuff. Great!' And it began to hum a Christmas carol. The City Slicker sulked. It was remembering last Christmas.

Last Christmas I'd been in Guadalajara. Guadalajara may sound like someone falling downstairs, but it feels like heaven. I'd been whisked off to Mexico by a generous benefactor. Gosh, I'd thought, this could be the start of something big. It was. It was the start of big gastroenteritis. The Christmas Dinner was dynamite: a beanfeast which almost reduced me to a has-been. One of Mexico's favourite dishes is Refried Beans. Fancy deciding to fry beans in the first place, and then getting all excited about the idea of frying *the same beans again*.

Anyway, my European sneers about the food were rewarded with a massive dose of Montezuma's revenge, which struck me a few miles up the road in Guanajuato. Guanajuato sounds like the noise the plumbing makes when the water's off: which it was, at the very moment we most needed it. What we had in Guanajuato was near enough to mod cons: add water and stir, and you'd have had a bathroom.

'It's fair enough, having gut-rot,' I mused between qualms. 'I mean, it's punishment for our colonial past. We shouldn't come here as fat, pampered tourists. I want to apologize all the time. I feel like saying, *Look here, for what it's worth, if I'd been Cortez, I'd have made a couple of documentaries and gone straight home.*'

After a few more hours of colic in a dry bathroom, the idea of going straight home had become irresistible. I did the best thing possible in the circumstances: I made an International Phone Call.

Me: 'Happy Christmas, Mum!'
Mum: 'What?'
Me: 'I said Happy Christmas!'
Mum: 'I can't hear you!'
Me: 'HAPPY CHRISTMAS!!'
Mum: 'What? – I think it's Sue.'
Me: 'I just rang up to say HAPPY CHRISTMAS!!!!'
Mum: 'What? Who is it? Is something wrong?'

At this point we were mercifully cut off. Mercifully because these tidings of comfort and joy had already set me back about £30. 'Fair enough, I suppose,' I'd said. 'After the centuries of oppression, why shouldn't we pay dearly?' All the same, it was only my benefactor who paid, since I didn't have a penny. I must have been really irritating company, alternately being ill and preaching at him, and never paying for anything. No wonder it wasn't the start of something big.

But despite the illness, the plumbing and the Refried Beans, Mexico had been wonderful: brown children running about under the orange trees; violet sunsets; fried shrimps on the seashore; tired Catholic bells, yellow stucco walls, and wrought-iron balconies exploding with geraniums. A glimpse of Paradise before the Fall. Or, in the Mexicans' case, before the earthquake. What sort of God would do a thing like that? Not the Christmas God, surely. Not good old Father Christmas. One of the Aztec Gods, may be: Mictlantecuhtli, the God of Death and Lord of the Underworld. Hang your stocking up for *him* and he'd leave a scorpion inside it.

Why is it that after every Paradise there has to be a fall? Why couldn't we start off face down in the dirt and end up under the orange trees in the deep green groves of contentment? I had that old falling feeling right now. Plunging hectically westwards like some dislocated star. Thrust out of another Eden. I could almost feel the evicting angel's hot breath on my neck as we fled towards the setting sun.

'Thijs heater is too strong,' complained my companion. 'Would you mijnd oepening your window?' I obeyed. I always obey foreigners. If you don't, they creep up the Thames at night and burn your boats.

I opened my window, and a rush of night air blew the last of the angel's hot breath away. Our headlamps were switched on. We were now in outer darkness: beyond the fug and thump of London. A tear fled down my face and splashed onto the cat at my side. Yes, there was a cat in the van with us. And it seemed only part of the spectacular nose dive my

8

fortunes were taking that this was not my favourite cat either. The favourite cat, along with my heart, soul, and roots, were left behind in London.

Ah, London. ('Don't!' shrieked the City Slicker, sticking its head under a cushion. 'I can't bear it!') When I'd first moved to London, five years ago, the exhilaration had swept me along so fast that I wasn't in two minds at all, for once. There was a rare mind-and-body consensus that London was, if not absolute heaven, a damned close thing.

Cities are, of course, designed for the young, solvent and fancy-free, and though I couldn't quite claim to be all that, there were a few years left before I was to become irrevocably middle-aged, bankrupt and leaden. When I first moved to London, I walked down the Mall one October twilight, and the trees and the traffic and the skyscrapers rising from the mists of blue were all exciting enough to give me a distinct sore throat. Or maybe it was the carbon monoxide.

Oh, the variety of it all! The dank smell of medieval stone at Westminster; jubilant marble angels up above; the square flash of Georgian windows; high heels in puddles; the romantic black secrecy of taxis, like the inside of a camera; the sudden warm green of the parks; the hectic din of restaurants; the smoky conviviality of the top of a lurching London bus; and below, the glassy palaces of Mammon glittering, inviting: Selfridges, Harrods, Coutts' Bank in the Strand.

I loitered among the Chinese smells of Soho, I peeped up at the pale and moody mansions of Belsize Park, I climbed the heights of Hampstead and gazed down upon the whole huge slumbering creature, and felt its hot heart beat. I loved old London with its sooty wharfs, and I adored the new London. The Empire had flooded in, with their spices and silks, the blood beat of reggae, the turban and the mask. They'd

9

saved the old city from atrophy and given it a transfusion of vitality so that it kicked and jumped. I darted in and out of the new coral caves, borne along by the surge of the tides, savouring the new saltiness.

I bought a house in a part of London which was now home to Asians, West Indians, Africans, Turks, Greeks and Orthodox Jews. Timidly I wondered if I could join the club. When I say 'I bought a house', however, what I really mean is, my ex-husband bought a house. He is a man who looks a bit like a pirate but has got the act slightly wrong: he robs himself instead of others. *Yo ho ho! Spanish Doubloons! How many would you like?* The house we bought was in Stoke Newington, then a fairly derelict and scruffy dump, but which has since risen in fashion so fast you can hear the pavements squeak. And they've changed the pavements, too, replacing the good old ordinary cracked stones with chic little dark-grey squares. So much more elegant to stub your Gauloise out on as you sit outside the wine bar. The cats who pad their way along among the Gauloise butts are now all sleek Burmese called Lao Tzu. When I moved in the cats were still all dreadful.

With my house I had also bought – unknown to me – two of the vilest cats in the world. These weren't cats, they were catastrophes: Ginger, an ex-male, and Pussy, an erstwhile female.

Unimproved by the middle classes, they had lived semi-wild in the garden, surviving on odd bits of chopped liver stolen from the kitchens of Jewish neighbours, and scowling at each other across a waste of weeds. I took them on because there seemed no alternative. And I had a kind of hope that with a lot of love and care and proper food and Adult Literacy Classes they might in time start to glisten and gleam and look splendid sprawled out on my dear old square piano, preferably in a pool of sunlight.

So much for liberal naïveté. Man may be perfectible but my cats certainly weren't. They grew fat and arrogant as well as retaining all their original vices. I was fond of Ginger, marginally the less hideous. His breath was so bad it was a miracle there was any paint left on the skirting boards, and he had a habit of vomiting onto people from a great height, but I liked him because he was shy and neurotic and kept out of my way.

Pussy, alas, was not only even more disgusting but catastrophically affectionate. A periodic mange gave her a bald and furious look. Severe catarrh – but let us draw a veil over that, and over the fleas which romped among her sludge-coloured thickets (or, in the mange season, wastes). Most of this would have been bearable were it not for her unconquerable love. She would run up people and bury her face in theirs, purring and sneezing like a very old and oily motorbike. Her claws were daggers and she drove them deeply into the laps of her victims. This was the creature sitting beside me in the hired van as we headed into the Western hills.

Why had I taken her? Well, Pussy and Ginger had been suing for divorce for years. Ginger was a very territorial guy, hanging out mostly in the garden and only coming indoors to be sick. Pussy, however, was deeply attached to people. Not individuals, you understand. She was shamelessly indiscriminating, throwing herself at anything in skin. So I reckoned she'd probably adapt better to wherever it was we were going, and left Ginger to lord it alone.

Goodbye, Ginger! When the film is made of his life, he will be played by Charles Bronson. But they'll really have to rough him up good first. Leave him out in the rain, thrash him with bicycle chains, sort of thing. Still, I'm sure Bronson will bear with it all in the interests of art.

Dear old cat! What fun we'd had back in Stoke Newington. I'd attacked the waste of weeds behind

11

the house and planted exotic bushes there. Ginger had kindly sprayed them. How deeply I'd enjoyed walking along Church Street, past shops full of chillies and yams and goat meat, in search of lily bulbs (and found them, no doubt, in a grocer's). How convenient to leap aboard a No. 73 bus and know that in only one and a half hours I could be outside Harrods, where, with any luck, that sensational pavement artiste, Lord Mustard, who looked and dressed like a traditional Tory Prime Minister complete with bowler and sad moustache, would be tap-dancing for a crowd of puzzled tourists. How delicious to jump off the homeward bus outside George's, the best fish-and-chip shop in North London. How—

'Ij doe not want to live in London,' my foreigner had said. 'Ij hav lived in cities too long. I want to be in natuur.' My world collapsed around my ears.

But I'm nothing if not a survivor. Nothing if not pusillanimous, compromising, treacherous and fickle. I winkled the dust of collapsed worlds out of my ears and discovered that if I hadn't exactly been in two minds about London all along, I had at least quite an advanced collection of suppressed misgivings. London is awful. Of course it is.

The vast distances, the constant crime, the triumph of the New Nastiness, the scrawled obscenity, the punk and the politician, the hypodermic and the disembowelled telephone. The wail of police sirens crying in the concrete canyons. The miles and miles of noise. Who would not wish to fly from all that? All the same . . .

'The park's very nice,' I ventured. 'And you can see the tops of the trees from here if you crouch on the top of the wardrobe.' The foreigner was not impressed with this argument. Clissold Park, it seemed, lacked the necessary precipes, gorges, flocks of goats and, above all, pure air. I knew what he meant. The only green thing about nearby Green Lanes these days is the faces of the pedestrians.

Here Fortune showed her hand. The piratical ex-husband decided that the time had come to sell our jointly owned house which he had never occupied, anyway. It wasn't his fault. Life in London is expensive and he had no alternative but to liquidize his assets before the slugs got at them. The house would have to go. What a household it had been, though, in its four years! I'll never forget the Brazilian sexologist, the Young Journalist of the Year, and the amazingly tall man in the raincoat who had all shared my roof and taken their turns to clear up Ginger's sick. But now that golden era was past. The house was put on the market at the very moment when classy Islington down the road became impossibly expensive, and was sold within a week despite its obvious flaws.

'I'm afraid the windows are only held together with paint,' I lamented, trying to hang on to my beloved house for a few more days. 'Oh no, they're really *not bad at all*,' said the terribly nice people whom Fortune had appointed to evict me. 'It's damp under the sink,' I persisted. 'Things without legs live down there. And things with too many legs. And these kitchen units are only horrible chipboard: it was all I could afford.' 'Oh, no, it's *lovely*!' they cried. And 'Oh, God, look at the *garden*!' They ran out of the back door and that was it. I knew I'd had my chips. For four years my garden had enjoyed all the time, energy and imagination I hadn't lavished on a husband, child or even self. It had come on quite a bit from the waste of weeds.

So out they ran, like Adam and Eve, and frolicked among the figs, apricots, jasmine, lilies, vines, apples, lavender, the purple spikes of *Salvia superba*, the grey lace domes of artemisia, the heavy pink, gloriously untidy globes of Madame Gregoire

13

Staechlin (an old rose, I hasten to add – not another exotic tenant). Come to think of it, it was winter at the time, so they couldn't have frolicked among anything much except a few dead stalks, but that made it even more poignant for me. I stroked Ginger's head. 'This is it, Ginge,' I whispered. 'This is the end of the road, old mate.' Ginge licked my hand, and sighed deeply. Three of my fingernails fell off. Never mind. I could always fling them on the compost heap – a final chivalrous gesture.

As the sale proceeded, chivalry gave way to cunning. Since the purchasers did not know the full horticultural madness they were poised to inherit, would it be all that unethical to roll the whole garden up like a giant carpet and take it with me? Mind you, the greenhouse would be a problem. Perhaps I could dismantle it and pile it up pane upon pane – a sort of glass lasagne. Tears poured down my cheeks so often I thought of installing a downpipe. This orgy of regret wasn't in any way unusual, though. I always get attached to the place where I happen to be, lingering sentimentally in hotel bedrooms and casting long looks backwards from the tops of buses to the bereft-looking bus stops where I so recently spent so many happy hours.

But on this Christmas Eve I didn't dare to cast sentimental looks back in the direction of London, let alone give serious thought to what I was leaving behind back there; the first house in my adult life where I'd felt really at home, together with the first garden I'd made from absolute scratch: from heaps of maggotty mattresses and sodden lino to lilies, roses and figs in four years. My fellow-gardeners can imagine the tearing sensation in the pit of my stomach. Being thrown out of the garden was not just an ancient myth, in my case. It was a here-and-now pain.

Apart from the more general charms of London,

most of my friends also lived there, within easy reach by bus, bike, tube or quaint rickety railway. I could also dash independently about and see all my writing contacts: producers, editors, predators, etc; score free lunches from large organizations, and even get odd bits of part-time work from institutions as different as Pentonville Prison and the BBC. (Not *all that* different, come to think of it.) London was where I'd learnt to live on my own, take care of myself, pay my way, go to bed alone without getting jumpy or depressed too often; to be, in short, in charge of my own destiny. Well, I mean as much as you can ever be, these days.

And now, in this westbound van on Christmas Eve, I wasn't even in charge of my own speed. The foreigner at the wheel was accelerating towards a motorway service station. The time had come for that most strenuous test of a relationship: fast food. I was nervous. I wasn't sure whether we even had a relationship to test, yet. Who was he anyway? And what was he going to think of British motorway food? In Holland motorway cafés offer you exquisite salads and spicy cakes. What would this mysterious Dutchman say when presented with the limp, glistening chip, the ferocious brick-red tea? And what was his name again? Well, let's call him Dick Van Dyke. (Not *the* Dick, you understand. Just *a* Dick. I mean – oh damn it, let's just call him Van Dyke.)

15

Chapter 2

Once I'd got beyond thirty-five I couldn't help noticing that I hadn't had a baby. At first I congratulated myself. None of my friends who'd had babies seemed to have survived intact. They did not come to the theatre any more. They were too tired to contemplate it. And I sometimes got the feeling that even if they weren't too tired, some of them wouldn't even particularly want to. Now isn't that weird?

And what had they gained in return? Children. I didn't mind admitting that children scared the hell out of me. The smaller they were, the more they scared me. Babies were the worst. They were so frail and so fierce all at once. They could snap like turtles, kick like donkeys, smile enchantingly at you one moment and the next, cover you from head to foot with a stream of sick. Their sudden shrieks could crack concrete and drown all adult conversation. There was nothing like a baby for bringing on one of my headaches.

It was unimaginable. I knew it was beyond me. Every day I saw young mums (increasingly young as time went on) trundling their buggies about and placating their tiny tyrants. I was awe-struck. How did they manage it? The constant responsibility, the noise, the pongs, the temptation to smack, the temptation to disappear for ever over the horizon. *Not for me*, I thought with a lucky grin, overtaking them with a bound and shooting off on some spontaneous pleasure trip to a bizarre boutique where the money I had not recklessly squandered on babycare requisites was soberly consigned to the necessaries of life, such as sequinned T-shirts.

Besides, the world was too crowded already. We must all do our bit, like the Chinese. And besides, I'd be such an appalling mother, oscillating between migraine and murder, it was a positive duty not to reproduce. Some women, I reckoned, were like sofas: destined to age in a worn but cosy way: buffeted and sat upon, kicked at and peed upon, comforting, soft, yielding, self-sacrificial, rarely re-upholstered, dear old long-suffering mums. And then there were the other women, like me and Jane Austen. She had genius to console her for her childlessness: I had potatoes in their jackets.

By the time I was thirty-six or so, it had occurred to me that I was thirty-six or so. I realized slowly but sickeningly that I had been sort of intending to get around to IT one day. Motherhood, I mean. When I was about fifty-six or so maybe. When I was rich enough to afford a nanny and a soundproof nursery. I would sit in my exquisitely underfurnished study (preferably overlooking the Mediterranean) and young Lorenzo would be brought in to give me a kiss before he went to bed. This was the kind of motherhood I had in mind.

By the time I was thirty-six and a half, I noticed that my current status was highly unpromising as far as babies were concerned. At the time I was single, and though there are more and more single parents managing to do a good job, I knew perfectly well that I hadn't a hope of bringing up a baby unless I had a

17

partner prepared to do his share of the cooking, washing, shopping and babycare – and preferably my share, too. As it was, not only did I have no such partner, but the occasional male persons who floated into my ken were quite spectacularly unsuitable.

Many of them were little more than children themselves. Younger men are such fun – and there are more and more of them around, I find. Mind you, preparing for a weekend of passion by buying in lots of packets of cereals (preferably those offering free dumper trucks) can become wearing after a while. And not many Younger Men are bursting to be fathers. Besides, it was bad enough having to mother a baby, let alone mother its father, too.

But the older men weren't too promising, either. Many of them had children already, elsewhere, and were understandably bruised. Or they'd got used to their bachelor comforts and what they wanted was a witty companion for dinner and the opera, not screams at 3 a.m. and strained carrot all over their Chinese silk wallpaper.

I discussed the situation with my friend Raymond in my moonlit garden one August night. 'I tell you what, Raymond,' I said. 'I'd quite like a child: you'd quite like a child; we both seem to fall in love with fairly unsuitable candidates for breeding purposes. We've known each other since the Early Middle Ages, your freckles don't disgust me all that much – supposing we don't manage to get it together over the next couple of years with anyone else, why don't we, you know, have one of those lovely eighteenth-century marriages? No jealous scenes: we'd each have our own carriage and no questions asked. And we could have a child together. What do you think?' Raymond took a deep drag on his cigarette, and muttered something brief. It sounded a bit like *Heaven Forbid*, but I expect I misheard.

'Ah well,' I resumed, 'wait and see, eh? As Shakespeare says, Time is the Whossname that will reveal all your thingummies. Or was it Doctor Johnson?'

'My dear,' observed Raymond at length, 'I must go to the lavatory.' That's the great thing about old friends. They never let moonlight go to their heads.

Time passed. The robin sang his autumn song. The leaves fell, the pound fell (though that is no longer merely seasonal). I decided to visit Amsterdam and renew acquaintance with an old friend, a composer of avant-garde music. You've guessed it – Van Dyke. Van Dyke is a name which certainly suits him, in view of his origins, which were well below sea level. His home village is so low-lying you have to drive there at 5 m.p.h. or you get the bends. Awfully flat, Holland. One tends to forget about it, don't you find? But there it is all the time, slowly extending itself into the North Sea. One day they'll bump into Yarmouth Pier and realize that it's time to call it a day.

Yes, Holland. Scarcely a promising source of second husbands, you may think. But think again. Because the Dutch have always cultivated, above all, the domestic virtues. They began by building themselves a country out of the sea, which illustrates the triumph of a domestic impulse over distinctly unpromising material. After the rigours of carving out a country from the watery deep, the task of putting up a few shelves or unblocking the drains please, darling, must be child's play.

You can see the Dutch are domestic, too, by the way they build their houses: beautifully. Huge windows to let in lots of light, and every window massed with houseplant foliage and elegant lace.

Amsterdam! Of all cities the cosiest! (Apart from the kidney-piercing wind that whips down the canals and forms icicles on all the bicycles.)

Dear Amsterdam! Intimate; egalitarian; foreign but not too foreign; secular, sensual; all that seventeenth-century brick and the glittering windows: what heaven! The only disadvantage of Amsterdam is the pavements: as rugged as the Appenines and generously garnished with what my mother, when pressed, refers to as dogs' business. The only danger in Amsterdam is that you will trip or slip and bash your brains out on the quaint, crazed, seventeenth-century bricks.

I was looking forward to my British Rail Three-Days-in-Amsterdam Special Excursion. I would be staying with Van Dyke. But there would be No Nonsense, of that I was sternly decided. I went to recuperate from and avoid emotion, and to contemplate seventeenth-century domestic architecture.

When I say Van Dyke was an old friend, I exaggerate slightly. He was more of an auld acquaintance. I had nearly known him for years. We had met occasionally and corresponded regularly. In fact, our correspondence had been more revealing than our meetings. Letter writing was a bit of a shared vice.

If my three days in Amsterdam got a bit sticky, I was confident that we could sit at opposite ends of the house and write each other letters. I was also confident that he wouldn't murder me with a meat-hook and keep me pickled in bits on the kitchen shelf – and of whom can one say that, these days? I knew he played the piano wonderfully, lived in a beautiful house, and made the sort of coffee that turns your bones to water (and, come to think of it, your water to bone). A soothing scenario for one who had been wrestling with the prospect of being thirty-seven, and lost.

I crossed the North Sea in a ship called the *St Nicholas*, fitted with the newest and best stabilizers you could get without a prescription. Nevertheless, it was not equal to the swell on this particular day. At one deep oceanic heave, all the flaps on the food counter swung open in unison and the cheese rolls, Scotch eggs, salads and cakes leapt out and flew across the room. Some even made it to the roof of the coffee machine, refused to come down, and started making demands.

I've never suffered from seasickness. It might be a consolation prize for having such bad migraines, which come at me out of the fog every month like a container truck storming down a ski slope with its brake cables cut. At least my migraines are fairly private, though. I crawl into the nearest black hole and lie there cursing the gods until it's time to come out again. Whereas people who are seasick are keen to share it. On this trip the corridors, the loos and the decks were all thronged with hectic green-faced folk offering to share their recent lunch with you. The café was the only safe place to be – apart from the flying cheese rolls.

I wrote a letter to my friend in London. 'I'm really looking forward to these three days.' My handwriting lurched as the ship plunged Neptunewards. 'Van Dyke's a good sort of bloke. Most Dutchmen are seven feet tall and rawboned, with rimless glasses. Van Dyke is more elfin. Perhaps it was the shortage of food during the war – yes, he can remember the war. Isn't that odd? But don't worry, I have no intention of succumbing to his pixie charms. He's not my type.'

Three days later, on the return trip, I found this letter still festering, unposted, in my handbag. I stared at it for a while and then added on the back of the envelope, 'PS, I have succumbed to his pixie charms after all.' On the way out I had thought of thirty-six reasons why succumbing in this way would be a very bad idea, and the first twenty-six were the North Sea. Still, I had felt safe, as I had already known him for years, and he was unquestionably not My Type.

But what was My Type? Was there such a thing? To tell you the truth, a couple of seconds' reflection is enough to reveal that over the years my affections

21

have been engaged with startling unpredictability. I began in my teenage years with dead homosexuals. (I liked a challenge.) Dag Hammarskjöld did not yield to my entreaties to meet me on the garage roof at midnight, in whatever ectoplasmic form he could muster, for a spiritual tryst. As I grew up, my appetites modified slightly to include the living – or in the case of John What's-his-name, the slightly living. By the time I got to Amsterdam I had mellowed even more.

But I still think I would have been all right if he hadn't started playing that Schubert. Schubert really is dangerous stuff. It has a dramatic effect on the aorta: squeezing the heart even more violently than digitalis. What's more, those British Rail Three-Days-in-Amsterdam tickets are a very bad idea. Three days is just long enough to take a leap in the dark and still be falling through the delicious darkness at going-home time. Three days is not long enough to hit the empty Coca-Cola cans and crisp packets at the bottom. At the end of my three days I was back on the North Sea. Or sort of. Actually I was coasting along a couple of feet above the waves. That's what love does. It makes a Hovercraft out of you.

The North Sea was still a problem. But Van Dyke showed a decided urge to cross it – yes, to rip himself up from his rhizomes and seek a new life in, of all places, the British Countryside. ('My Dear!' screamed the City Slicker. 'Can he be *entirely sane*? Why should a man in his position wish to install himself among damp hills when he could fly like a bird to Paris or New York? It can't be your potent charms, surely?') Clearly not. There were reasons for wishing to leave Holland.

Apart from the flatness, the cabbages, and the egalitarianism, he had private reasons of his own. Nothing sensational: just the usual. A sense of *déjà vu*, a vague touch of anomie, a desire to escape a place already riddled with associations, most of them painful. 'Ah, the Eerste Weteringsdwarsstraat!' (that's the name of one of Amsterdam's unpretentious little streets, by the way). 'Where Saskia threw the *Fatsia japonica* at my head! Ugh, the Passeerdersgracht! Where my second best bike skidded on some Alsatian's business and flung me headlong into the canal.' (Or, as the Dutch would have it, hoedlong op de kanaal. What a charming language! They sound as if they're speaking underwater – which is, when you think of it, understandable.) Anyway, he'd assured me, he would be delighted to leave Amsterdam. Though by now (little short of Swindon) he was probably beginning to have second thoughts. Here we were, parking our van in a motorway service station, heading for our destiny, probably with chips and peas.

I stole a sidelong glance at Van Dyke. His nose was still retroussé – or, if you prefer it, snub. Or as the Dutch call it, with the ineffable elegance of their lingo, *Snotneus*. In fact, it was even snubber than mine. I wasn't sure that, genetically speaking, this was such a terribly good idea. Yes, genetics had reared its ugly head. He had had a dream that we had had a child, and for old hippies like us that was as good as an order. With such snubs in the ancestry, though, what chance did any baby have of possessing a nose which actually kept the rain out? It worried me.

I also felt a lot of patriotic guilt that I hadn't managed to fix myself up with a good old British-made partner, and had instead imported an exotic Continental model for whom it would obviously be much more difficult to get spare parts. It also struck me with a sickening thud that if I were to say to him, 'Viv Richards is on a pair and Emburey's on a hat-trick!' he would not grasp the momentousness of the moment. All right, I admit it. Even before we were married I was already planning to talk about cricket with other men, behind his back.

Chapter 3

We faced each other over our Minestrone soup and Croutons. (There! Croutons! You see, you Continentals? We Brits learn fast. It's only forty years since the war and already we've mastered Minestrone and cultivated the Crouton.)

'Excjuse me,' ventured Van Dyke. 'What is Welsch Rarebit? Is ijt a Welsch Disch?'

'Not now!' I cried, staring into his eyes for all I was worth. I was trying to recapture that first, fine, careless rapture. The fluorescent lighting was against us, though, since it makes everyone look about ninety-five years old. And just think (now here's a novelty): it would only be fifty years till Van Dyke *actually was ninety-five*! Yes, he was that miraculous thing: already over forty.

Forty is a bit like Death. It's somehow The Beyond, and one's terribly grateful to those friends who experience it first. *Well*, you think, *if he's done it, I can do it too.* Here was Van Dyke: well over forty and yet drinking his soup with apparent relish and not a dribble. What's more, he could *remember the war*. Perhaps that's why he was enjoying his soup so much. Yes, he could remember the Germans occupying his village. It was like having supper with a TV documentary.

'It will be fantastiek to be in Wales,' he purred. 'In natuur.' Reluctantly I abandoned my scrutiny of his ancient but handsome façade, and my speculations about his extraordinary childhood ('Ij cocked a snoek at the Gestapo and threw a kohlrabi stalk at the Obergruppenfuhrer's Kollaborator-Girlvriend ...'). What I had to contemplate, nay, get to grips with, was my own immediate future, in Wales.

You may wonder why we were headed for South Wales. And when I say South Wales I don't mean airy Pembrokeshire where the smart set go for holidays ('Nearleh got drined but supah realleh!'). Nor the Wye Valley, where Wordsworth got the hots for ruined abbeys. We were headed for the Valleys: Neath, to be exact. And say what you like about Neath, it is modestly named. In fact, Neath has a ruined abbey of its own, every bit as impressive as Wordsworth's, but I was not to know that – yet.

We had been offered a friend's cottage as a temporary bolt hole while we looked for somewhere permanent. This friend, who had recklessly introduced me to Van Dyke several years before, was a charming Welsh person addicted to women, mountaineering and the class struggle, preferably all at once. However, at this moment, he'd hung up his crampons and plunged with generous abandon into matrimony.

His former bachelor house had been for sale for months: empty and abandoned. It was a terraced cottage in a tiny village. The housing market in South Wales tends to be sluggish because nobody has any money, or work, or hope. You don't buy yourself a new house in such circumstances. You make yourself a tent out of the curtains, just in case, and hope the loan company won't try to repossess the baked beans you fed to your children last week.

What our friend Byron needed (he was also, in his spare time, a man of letters) was a tenant or two who could live for a while in his still For Sale house, and welcome prospective buyers in with gently smiling jaws. It was a small house, so we had to store most of our big furniture. Van Dyke had a grand piano and an architect's drawing-table upon which he composed either avant-garde music or modernist housing schemes – it was hard to tell just by looking. Into the warehouse also went my nineteenth-century piano, harmonium, boxes of old love letters and bits of used sticking plaster (I find it really hard to part with anything). We travelled to Wales with a few sticks of furniture, a few sticks of cat, and a couple of dying typewriters.

We reached the house at midnight, unpacked the van with Byron's help (a fridge under one arm and a cooker under the other) and, having waved goodbye and thanks to our landlord, fell exhausted into where the bed would've been if we'd had time to assemble it. The window was full of black sky. Outside, slumbering, was Clwch. No, that's not a misprint, it's the name of the village. I couldn't wait for daylight, when Clwch would be revealed in all its granite, moss and Methodism.

Dawn came, and we gazed out at a lovely sheep-strewn mountain. There was a chapel, phone box, and next door the General Store and Post Office. We were really into the action here! There was street life. Several times a day people passed our front windows, and if we were really lucky we might see someone parking a car. Maybe I wasn't going to miss Piccadilly Circus that much after all. The back of the house overlooked a valley and forested hillside beyond. The tiny garden could, with a lot of work, eventually have become a quite elegant little builders' yard. But what did that matter? With a whole hillside of spruces for the eye to travel across, who needs *Fatsia japonica*?

I had always loved Wales. My mother grew up on a farm in Montgomeryshire. I later discovered that the real Welsh hardly recognized Montgomeryshire as theirs, being impossibly far east, something little short of Moscow. Besides, who would want to claim a deserted landscape of bog and pine, curlew and Roman stone? The answer was me, of course. As a bald but sensitive baby I was taken to meet my Welsh grandmother and a galaxy of fat little uncles with names like Dai and Ieu. The ancestral farm, called something like Abercadaber, was quite magical, with black and white timbers, a large brown pool patrolled by flotillas of fierce geese, and huge barns full of banks of grain to slide down.

I was captivated, and lived every year for the summer holidays, when we would be released from brick suburbia into the pale green light of Wales, to explore the rusting water butt, the ferns, the Roman stones, the slugs. Various aunts and uncles lived even deeper into Wales, and it was with great delight that I dodged the drizzle in Dolgellau, running up and down the steep little granite streets, leaping over roadside torrents, eating chip-shop chips, and driving past the towering mass of Cader Idris to visit the beach at Fairbourne, where a great skyful of western light danced on the waves and the estuary birds wheeled and squealed above our picnicking heads.

As I stood at our back door all those years later in the Neath Valley, drawing in great lungfuls of forest air, I felt a brief leap of exhilaration. Had I come home? Not in the trivial, materialist, London-is-Wonderful sense but in the deep bred-in-bone-and-blood sense. Wales was, after all, the Land of my Mothers; the place where, as a child, I'd most loved to be. In the past I'd often been told I was a real Celt (at least, I *think* that's what they said). Was my off-white skin and my love of rain and rugby football suddenly beginning to make sense? Was this the return of the Prodigal Daughter? Would my fellow-Welshies kill the fatted calf and welcome me back with brimming eyes?

'Oh my God – there's nothing to eat!' I gasped. It still seemed to be Christmas Eve. I expect we'd travelled through a time zone, or something. Anyway, knowing that due to Christmas, New Year and St David's Day the shops were about to close for something like three months, I hastened to make up a list of the things with which we city-dwellers tend to conjure up a pastoral breakfastoral: *All Bran. Bran. Bran Flakes (but that's another story). Wholemeal Flour. Brown lasagne. Veg. & Fruit. Decaffeinated Coffee. Herbal Tea. Baked Beans. Wholemeal Eggs. Brie. Gouda. Polyunsaturated Face Cream.*

And then I nipped round to the village shop next door. 'I'll go!' I cried to Van Dyke, who was installing draught excluders between the banisters. After all, I was the Real Celt. I was the returned exile, brimming with joy and ready to hurl myself face down on my native soil and kiss it, much as the Pope salutes the airport tarmac of each new country he visits. (By the way, don't you find that encouraging? After all, if a man will kiss tarmac, there's hope for us all.)

Ah, the smell of village shops! That slightly-damp-old-cardboard, paraffin-and-candles smell. The lady in charge gave me a broad smile, probably for Byron's sake, and after some introductions I launched into my list.

'Have you got any All Bran?'

'No, sorry. We don't get much call for it round here.'

'No, of course not. I hate it anyway. Er . . . how about lasagne?'

'Pardon?'

'The . . . er . . . vegetables. What have you got?'

'Not very much, I'm afraid. It being Christmas you see. Just that cauli and a few turnips.'

'Turnips! Heavenly! I'll have a pound.'

My eye rested nervously on the cauliflower. It obviously had suffered a history of abuse, and even at the start of its long and eventful life had not enjoyed particularly good health. I did not want to reject the cauliflower. But I suddenly realized that trips to the village shop were fraught with sociological implications. If I didn't buy the cauli, would she think I was sneering down my nose at it? If I did buy it, would she think I had more money than sense? If I didn't buy it, would it bankrupt her? If I did buy it, would I be depriving old Mrs Lloyd the Bungalow of a nourishing soup?

I panicked and consulted my list, though even I knew by now that it was madness to do so.

'Er . . . Brie?'

'Pardon?

How idiotic of me. I gazed desperately round the shelves.

'Ah, yes – there! Brie-llo pads, please.' Oh hell. I could just see the scenario that would unfold behind my back in a few minutes' time, when her next customer arrived.

'Her next door was in here just now. Wanted some *Breello* pads, if you please!'

'*Breello* pads? Never! Who's posh!' I thrust the dreadful list into my pocket and looked about me. The shop seemed to stock mainly tins of rice pudding and shampoo.

'Oh! Marvellous! I'll have a couple of those amusing little tins of raice parding.'

What was happening to me? I seemed to be succumbing to some kind of deadly virus. I seemed to be getting a fatal case of the British Raj. It had already taken hold of my larynx and was swooping downwards. I could positively feel my ankles thickening.

29

The only thing missing was the racial confidence – and believe me, without it, going down with a bad case of the British Raj is really *bad news*.

'Anything else?'

'Neh thenks, actuallah, thet's all.'

'Right. That'll be two pounds ninety-eight.'

Two pounds ninety-eight?? For a pound of turnips, a box of Brillo pads and a couple of tins of rice pudding? Was that right? Or was this the British Raj price? Having given up Maths at the age of twelve to do Ancient Greek, I was not in a position to argue. Not even in Ancient Greek.

'Heah you are. Supah. Thenks offleh.' And I escaped, clutching the Brillo pads tightly to my chest. They were, after all, probably the highest-fibre items in the shop. Though I doubted whether even Van Dyke's culinary skill could transform them into the vegetarian pasta dish of my dreams.

We drove off secretly to Neath, found a Tesco and smuggled three carrier bags full of smart food home under our cagoules. Paranoia was setting in. (A lovely name for a girl, don't you think? In fact, wasn't she in the *Odyssey*? Or am I thinking of Nausea?) Several villagers peered in through the front window to observe our simple, brown, fibrous meal and by decaffeinated coffee time I was having serious second thoughts about net curtains. Like most liberals, I have always ripped net curtains down, crying *What do we have to hide*? But suddenly it seemed we had a great deal to hide: chiefly ourselves.

So after lunch I compromised and erected a screen of house plants dangling from Oxfam macramé holders, which covered the whole window. This attracted even more attention from the locals since, I realized in a flash, rampant foliage is a middle-class affectation. In fact, a window-full of greenery was probably the most provocative thing, sociologically speaking, that I could have installed. But I couldn't take it down again, could I? Or the whole village would see me ironing our permacrumple 100 per cent cotton Third World Batik shirts – *on the floor.* (We had forgotten the ironing board.)

What we need, I meditated as I ironed away, is 80 per cent Marlon and 20 per cent Anodyne shirts that hang over the bath and drip dry. We could also do with some 80 per cent Lysistrata, 20 per cent Formica net curtains that hang in the window and never even need painting. Not to mention – but at this point, blinded by culture shock, I made a false stroke and ironed the cat. Actually, it was quite an improvement. I wished I'd thought of it before. Though I'm sure everyone else in Clwch (at least, if they had any sense) had 100 per cent Feel-yne drip-dry cats. I put the iron away (what Van Dyke would call leaving it lying about) in a mood of great perplexity.

I had somehow lost my grip on everything. Was I not a real Celt after all? My white skin and dark hair, my love of rain and rugby football, suddenly did not seem enough. I missed London with a mighty pang. There were all sorts of foreigners there. Here, there was only me.

And, of course, Van Dyke. But he was all right, being a *real* foreigner. Dutch colonial history does not include South Wales. People liked him. People always seem to like him much more than they like me. I think this is because he's basically a hell of a lot nicer.

Whenever I burst into tears of homesickness he would make me a cup of tea and offer me lengths of draught excluder (I did wonder about knitting myself a winter coat out of the stuff). Whenever it was mild – as it was often that winter and spring – he would take me on wonderful trips into the countryside.

The charms of Wales were all around us. As we walked along the sea cliffs of the Gower Peninsula, or panted up steep forest tracks, or picnicked among

31

huge rocks and waterfalls, there were moments of perfect happiness. When Nature lays it on so thick, a sense of cultural uneasiness pales into insignificance.

But despite all the beauty, I was not at ease in Wales. The ferns and the foxgloves of my childhood were still there, but I realized now that having spent my early years in the suburbs of the Home Counties, I was not just not Welsh, as I had always fondly imagined, but even worse I was, especially in politically alert South Wales, the enemy. I smelt of colonialism, at least to myself; like a person suddenly aware that their T-shirt stinks and they haven't got a spare one with them.

Finding myself surrounded by the unemployed ex-working class, impoverished by decades of greedy industrial policy (ruin the landscape and grab all the coal you can get, and then get out quick and leave them to it), I instantly began to feel effete, absurd and grotesquely overprivileged. If I was a man I'm sure I'd have laid myself down in front of the local youths and invited them to kick me to death. The trouble with the English class system is that it makes you feel bitter if you're underprivileged and guilty if you're not.

Seated at my (oh God! – desk, but keep it quiet), I stared out of the back window and down to the stream. The baby oak trees were all waiting for spring. It was all so promising. Surely I was being paranoid? I was not trying hard enough. I had half an eye on the Exit sign, and they seemed to sense it. I would damn well force myself to make a go of it. Settle down properly. Stop apologizing. Commit myself.

When we got around to the serious business of house-hunting, Van Dyke suggested that we start by seeing what we could afford in Wales, and I gritted my teeth and agreed. This was my big chance. It might be hard, but wasn't that the only way one ever learned anything? I loved Wales still. I was just convinced, at the moment, that I was not *worthy* to love her. I must put such agonizings aside, and get stuck in.

I pulled on the only pair of boots not already covered in mountain. I had bought them in the heart of London's most filthy-rich West End: in South Molton Street. They were scarcely suitable for storming the hill farms, being metallic-silver with high heels, as might be worn by a visitor from the Planet Krull. But, oh dear, it was going to be a long time before I felt as much at home as *that*.

Chapter 4

Our first property sounded large and modernized and enjoyed 'an elevated position with outstanding views'. Why, then, was it only £35,000? We turned off the main road. Up and up we went: higher and higher; beyond the tundra, beyond the Yeti. A sheer precipice yawned to our right, the road unfenced and covered with black ice. 'Don't drive so fast,' I shrieked, as we crawled round a bend at 2 m.p.h. 'I think I haav been here bevore,' murmured Van Dyke. 'It is in the Ardèche.' What was this? The sense of *déjà vu* that precedes sudden, violent death?

Not a moment too soon we reached our journey's end. We were so high up now we were practically in orbit. In fact, we were probably on the Planet Krull itself. The house was built on the mountain top with abysses on all sides. I closed my eyes and groped for the garden gate. Indoors, a perfectly nice, normal woman was frying pork chops. 'I was a bit surprised you managed to get up here today,' she beamed, as if visitors regularly plummeted to their doom. 'No, we don't have gas up here.' *Not even oxygen*, I thought, as my brain turned blue. Why were they selling? 'Well, to be honest ... we want to go a bit ... er ... lower down.'

It seemed a bit premature, not to say presumptuous, to hang about at heaven's gate, so as soon as politely possible we fled to the valley floor. I kept my eyes firmly shut until we were back on the A474.

Thank God, the next place was low-lying. Well, 'up a short hill' were the estate agent's words, but after what we'd been through it seemed more like down a deep hole. I was mystified by the lack of praise on the estate agent's sheet. An old farmhouse with one and a half acres for only £27,000 ... how could an estate agent possibly have failed to find anything attractive to say about it?

The moment we set foot across the threshold it all became clear. The most nauseating smell in the world zoomed up our nostrils: the smell of boiling bulldogs. The kitchen was full of bulldogs and the saucepans on the stove seemed full of simmering ex-bulldog. How long could we hold our breaths? Long enough to see the entire house?

We raced, as breathlessly as possible, from room to room. 'This is the main bedwoom' – a pile of bulldog-scented junk. 'These are the kiddies' wooms' – mountains of smaller, smellier junk. 'And now, I'm afwaid this woom is a bit of a mess – it's the junk woom.' Old tricycles, gutted sofas, disembowelled lawnmowers and bits of old bulldog formed a tottering pagoda which almost touched the ceiling.

'Now I'll show you the paddocks,' threatened our guide. His work was the breeding of horses and dogs, and the house was surrounded by decaying caravans and rusting wheel-less Cortinas full of straw and more bulldogs. 'You might be able to do something with that,' he suggested as we passed a dung-encrusted caravan. *Not without an Exocet missile*, I thought, as the mud reached my armpits.

At this moment the inevitable happened: Van Dyke trod on an animal. Luckily it was only a non-

35

commercial cat. There was only one foal this year: it had not been a good season for horsebreeding. In the circumstances it seemed a triumph that anything had bred at all: anything with legs, that is. On the way out we passed an evil-looking concrete bunker containing yet more bulldogs, but somehow managed not to break into a run. Perhaps it was the ten inches of mud on the soles of our boots.

By now we were feeling deeply chastened. The awful puzzled look of those sad-eyed horses standing in a lake of mud: the desperate out-of-control escalation of the kingdom of bulldog, and the sense that hysterical squalor must sooner or later break out into some kind of domestic violence, will pursue me for ever.

'I've had enough for today,' I shivered. 'Those poor people! Fancy living like that! How will they ever sell it? Let's go home.'

'Just one more place,' suggested Van Dyke. 'Ijt is only a couple of miles away, so ijt would be wasting petrol not to goe.' I had already learnt not to argue with statements like that. So, reluctantly, I perused the estate agent's blurb.

'It says semi-rural.' That sounded appealing. Not too rural, thanks very much. The whitewashed farmhouse in the photograph looked quite pretty. Semirural. Reassuring. What it turned out to mean was, so impossibly remote that the solitude would drive you screaming bananas after five minutes. But by now we must have been already slightly insane, for at the bottom of the track we parked the car and decided to walk up – even though we could not see the actual house. We saw its name-board though: Hendre Caradoc. 'Henry Carruthers,' murmured Van Dyke. I rather liked the idea of a house called that.

We set off. At first lush rhododendrons raised our hopes but they soon gave way to stunted thorn bushes and eagles. My Krull boots began to take their

36

toll and after about three miles of mincing through the rocks, all I could hope for was amputation. At length the house appeared up ahead: dead white against the bare mountain slopes, surrounded by shrieking winds. In one of the bedroom windows something flashed. An axe being sharpened? If there were a Crippen or a Christie waiting for us up there, what were our chances? You'd need Sherpas and a grant from the Royal Geographical Society just to get back to the 'B' road. I didn't fancy having to pull up my Krull boots and mince for my life.

A tall thin man admitted us. His nose was long and red with cold, and his coat was tattered at the back, like a bird whose tail had been torn in a fight. Our hearts were immediately touched with anguish and the desire to escape, but we had to go through with the charade. It might have been preferable to be hacked to bits by a mad axeman, after all.

His bewildered-looking teenage children were huddled up round the TV like puppies at their mother's dugs, drinking in the promise that somewhere Out There was a world. Way Out There, in this case. The house, though small, was only half-inhabited despite the three children. They all congregated in one room, as if the desolation of their surroundings required constant human contact.

Once more we trekked to inspect the paddock, stumbling through frozen tussocks to a forlorn vegetable patch where a few dwarf stumps of plant life couched pitifully against the blast. 'Oh, broccoli! How marvellous!' I cried inanely – the last gasp of civilized speech I could muster.

It was extremely difficult, when being shown round these weird and terrifying places, to sustain the pretence that not only were we not disgusted or scared or deeply sympathetic, but we actually admired the whole thing no end and were already fantasizing about creating an Alpine bed amongst the wreckage of old glaciers in the third bedroom. It was even impossible, afterwards, for us to speak about it at all for several hours until we had recovered.

Had these three families (all English, incidentally) come here in pursuit of some half-imagined idyll, taken on too much and been worn down by the impossibility of it all? The first house we visited had already been on the market for a year, and we didn't even dare to ask about the others. Our day's house-hunting had left me feeling as if a Shakespearean tragedy had unfurled before me: I was drained, torn between pity and terror. And longing for South Molton Street, in the heart of London's West End, where I had bought the Krull boots (which now lay mangled in the hall like a couple of baby crocodiles who had fought to the death in a sewer). Dear London! It did welter in hideous Babylonian pride, of course. But at least there were a few other people about.

'I think,' I ventured over the last of the tinned rice pudding, 'that this business of English people buying up Welsh farmhouses is not necessarily the answer. I mean, lovely though the countryside is, the iso-lation . . .'

'Ja, ja. Bezides, none of thijs houses had roem for my grand piano and arkitekt's drawijng-table.'

'Well, there you are, then. And besides . . . we both need to go to London now and then and it's awfully expensive from way out here.'

I had hit him where it hurt: in the purse. Our purses were to become even more painful as time went on. Isn't it odd how when we were young we had no money and it seemed like heaps, whereas now we're cruising towards middle age we have what ought to be plenty and it disappears like magic?

'The other thing is, all this Forestry Commission plantation is a bit depressing, don't you find?'

He gave me a sharp look, as well he might. I

already suffered from primordial depression for twenty days a month. And he came from a village where the dear old Dutch farmers and their wives regularly went off and pegged themselves out in the barn.

'Why don't we hang on to the principle of living in the country, but start looking a bit further east: in Gloucestershire and Somerset, for example?' My heart gave a secret bound at the mere thought of the tame green lanes, medieval limestone manors and hidden gardens of my native county.

'Is Gloucestershire mountainous?'

'Oh, yes. Well, by your standards, anyway. Steep, at any rate. And Somerset even has a gorge. A bit like the Grand Canyon, only slightly smaller. And no poison ivy.'

Van Dyke graciously consented to my plan and immediately I rushed to the phone and called about twenty new estate agents. When they heard what size of house we wanted and the amount of money we could command, several of them sneered and one actually sniggered. I didn't care. Let them sneer. I was so relieved at the prospect of giving up all pretensions of Welshness, that I gabbled and capered like a monkey. Going home! I was going home! I didn't know exactly where that was, of course. But you get the general idea.

Chapter 5

So I wasn't Welsh. So what? Fifteen years ago I'd have felt guilt and regret. In our idealistic twenties we all wanted to dive headlong into the Working Class, where Real People were to be found complete with curlers, beer and hearts of gold. Belonging to the wretched Middle Classes, of course, we ourselves were stuck with hearts of cardboard. Mine didn't so much beat as rattle like a half-empty carton of cornflakes.

The idealistic twenties soon gave way, thank God, to ways of life noticeably more murky and compromising. By now, pushing forty, I realized that you couldn't put a square peg in a round hole, and that inverted snobbery was no better than the other sort. It might have been wonderful being born into the Celtic fringe instead of Home Counties suburbia, but on the other hand, it might have been mystifying and draughty.

I wouldn't for a moment claim that anything like wisdom was stealing o'er my soul: it was something more like weariness. Some places feel like home: some don't, and as the forties begin to roar what one wants above all is to be, in some final sense, seated at the hearthstone with the door firmly bolted against the blast.

What is home, anyway? It seems to me that what turns out to be home isn't necessarily where you grew up. It's more a case of finding the sort of place which suits the person you've turned out to be. Like many people who grew up in the suburbs, I felt alienated from them at the time. But then, being an adolescent, one is more or less inevitably at odds with one's surroundings.

My uneasiness with the suburbs has lasted into early middle age, but it's only modern suburbs that give me the jitters. A nice mature Edwardian suburban semi, clouded with laurel and laburnum, with idiosyncratic gables, a pantry, and a Labrador called Daphne next door could feel exactly like home. And in a way that's how I felt about marriage, too. Yes, for me marriage offered identical pleasures to those of the Edwardian suburb.

Being single had been like a touring holiday, with new landscapes unfolding around every bend in the road, with no one to please but myself and no obligation to consult anyone or anything save the *Michelin guide*. But eventually even the freedom and novelty of a holiday begins to pall, and one longs for home: the reassuring weighty tick of the grandfather clock, the smell of coats in the hall, the familiar muddle of the cupboard under the stairs. Even so did I now begin to turn towards the idea of marriage again, but this time, I hope, with fewer delusions and more patience.

Like my historical heroine Elizabeth I, I liked the idea of an alliance with the Low Countries. There's something doughty and reliable about the Dutch, and surely at my advanced years it was a better plan to marry into a nation who spend their time reclaiming old swamps than, say, lying around in gondolas singing arias. The longer I spent with Van Dyke, the more he revealed himself as not just a funny foreigner who said things like, 'These stairs are dangerous: some of the barristers are heavily infested with woodworm.'

Yes: beyond the howlers which the poor chap threw up in his continuing struggle with the mystery of domestic and idiomatic English, a fully three-dimensional human being was slowly revealing itself. He even laughed at his own howlers when they'd been explained to him, which is, you'll agree, pretty damned human. And though he could be shrewd and practical when it came to keeping the east wind off his kidneys, and could put up the straightest shelves in the world, he was also, it seemed, something of a romantic – well, by Dutch standards, anyway.

'Look at thijs fantastiek old tree!' he cried on one of our walks in the Gower Peninsula, the tears glistening in his eyes as he stared up into the great grey architecture of an ancient ash tree.

'Thijs mountains are zo beautiful!' he would exult, leaping from rock to rock like an ibex. And if we met any small children, he'd zoom off with them in an instant, running races, listening to their plans, tossing them in the air and playing endless tedious childhood games with them without a murmer of discontent.

Confront Van Dyke with an old lady hesitating at a kerbside and he'd whisk her across the road with a charming smile and a compliment to send her on her way. If a stray dog limped up to him, Van Dyke would take the thorns out of its paw, carry it off to the vet for a course of expensive antibiotics, and get bitten for a week afterwards administering them.

Enthusiastic about nature, and chivalrous towards the weaker forms of creation, Van Dyke completed his romanticism with the most pure and ardent socialism I'd encountered since the Sixties. Needless to say he found the current British Government quite astonishingly evil, and could not watch the TV news without crying out in pain and indignation.

'They are putting up the Old Age Pension only sixty-five p!' he would roar. 'Ijt is an obscenity! Jesus Christus, this minister must be shot. Get me a gun and I will do it.'

It was becoming clear that I was living with a man whose heart was in the right place. His pyjamas were also in the right place: neatly folded under his pillow. Now on this point, I have to admit, I hesitated for a moment. Since I'd started to co-exist with Van Dyke something strange had happened. His possessions were always folded, smoothed and neatly aligned with the prevailing environment: even the papers on his desk were all set out perpendicularly in order, parallel with the desk's edges. Nay, his very underpants were parallel with the interior of their drawer.

But what had happened to my possessions in the meantime? A poltergeist appeared to be involving itself in my affairs. Wasn't that my copy of Coleridge's poems lying open and face down under the cat? Weren't those my tights dangling mysteriously from the curtain rail? Why was the bedroom door so hard to open? Could it be the ball of dirty underwear wedged underneath it?

Why was my desk scattered with old bus-tickets and tattered third-hand used envelopes? Was some sacrifice taking place? To the gods of disorder, perhaps? Was I – and the possibility zipped up and down my spine several times like an electric train on the point of blowing a fuse – was I, could I possibly be . . . a child of Dionysus, after all?

The more I lived with Van Dyke, the more it seemed I could be. Well, as near to Dionysus as anyone could be who only manages a glass of white wine and soda once a week. Mind you, after my glass of white wine and soda I do tend to hurl myself headlong into the nearest herbaceous border and recite Byron to the Begonias. How very different all this was to what I had recently known, though. My last *mésalliance*, you see, had been with Dionysus himself: a crazed comic genius, a Welsh wizard who lived in San Francisco and thought nothing of four bottles a day.

He was wonderful, of course: he was a force of nature. But what an unpleasant creature I had turned into at his side! Cradling my tonic and tonic with an expression of reluctant tolerance on my pursed lips. Planning my next suggestion: *Do you think we should go home? It is three a.m., after all. Wouldn't you like something to eat? It might make you feel, er, better. Don't you think you could do with some sleep?*

It had been my turn, then, to cling to order. Apollo, the god in the white cricketing flannels with the Brilliantined hair and immaculate whitened boots, had invaded my being. I had become the Head Prefect, the schoolmarm, the nanny, the sour, constipated perfectionist Site Foreman, anticipating everything, arranging everything. My soul was neatly folded away in its box.

But now I was all loose and earthy all over the place. My shoes lay where they were kicked. I scribbled on scraps of paper and then lost them. The western wind blew my hair into elf-knots. I read Coleridge in the bath. I dropped Coleridge in the bath. I didn't care. Neither did Coleridge. I lurched around punning brilliantly. I was a four-cups-of-cocoa a day man. I slept late, and when the post came I threw the bills up in the air. I kicked or caressed the cat according to my mood. This was real life, dammit.

It is odd how radically we can change according to who we're with. Perhaps in every relationship there has to be an irresponsible lazy hedonist and a Head Prefect. Well, all I can say is, let the other fellow be the Head Prefect. I'd rather have someone tut-tutting over my mess than fret and nag over someone else's.

So dear old Van Dyke, apart from all his other virtues, had brought out the beast in me, thank goodness. He was a much better Head Prefect than I had ever been, so with relief I relinquished the post and went off to roll in the mud with the piccaninnies. Metaphorically speaking, of course.

And yet (and permit me one final coda to this catalogue of Van Dyke's virtues) despite his neat methodical ways with draught excluder and paper clips, Van Dyke had unsuspected depths of lovable absent-mindedness. He would hang the front door keys neatly on their nail and forget to take them out with us. (Of course I would forget, too, but it was my privilege to forget – it's a full-time job reeling about in Dionysian oblivion.)

'God Allemachtig!' he would exclaim. 'I have forgotten the keys.' Now, after an eight-mile hike in the rain across a mountain range, this is not exactly what you want to hear, shivering on your doorstep and panting for dry socks and cups of tea.

'Wait! I thijnk I can break in!' Being light and monkey-like in physique, and having done rock-climbing in the Ardèche, Van Dyke shinned up the drainpipe, abseiled along a windowsill and daintily raised the window I had so Dionysianly left unbolted.

'See?' I cried, as he disappeared within. 'If I hadn't left my window open, where would we be now? There's more to life than avoiding draughts, you know,' I went on, waiting for him to nip downstairs and let me in. 'Anyway, I like draughts. Within reason. Round me head, at least. They're a message from the wild and whirling world of Nature we're all caught up in. At least we Dionysians are. Come on, open the door! I'm freezing to death out here. This bloody wind's coming straight down off Crag Peryllws.' He didn't let me in for ages, though. So forgetful.

Right then, I thought, staring into space in bed one

45

morning while Van Dyke did his Swedish Army drill exercises. Thump-thump-thump BOING. Thump-thump-thump BOING. Every BOING was a great leap skywards, knees raised. Would he crack his head on the ceiling? Would he strike his chin with his knees and splinter his beautifully maintained teeth?

During the Thump-thump-thumps the wardrobe displayed a disturbing tendency to waltz away from the wall and shimmy towards him like an over-excited spacecraft. Would its door swing open, Van Dyke bound inside, and the whole bedroom fill with unearthly light as he was beamed off to another galaxy? On headachy mornings I certainly hoped so.

Right then, I thought. Is this IT? Can this be Love? BOING! Can this be the Thump-thump-thump that leads to the altar, or in our case, the Registrar's Desk? I must be careful not to BOING in where angels fear to thump-thump-thump. On the other hand, he keeps asking me to marry him and, who knows, no one else ever might. And if he gets to know what I'm really like, perhaps he'll change his mind. Especially if I lie festering in bed every morning instead of going thump-thump-thump and keeping myself in trim.

Well, it was clear enough that, objectively viewed, Van Dyke was far too good for me, but I musn't let that kind of moral scruple interfere with naked self-interest.

'Whew! I hav finished. I will go and get the breakfast. Would you lijk an egg, darling?' Right. He'd do.

First, though, I felt I really had to listen to a bit of his music – much in the way that Americans go in for premarital blood tests.

'I want to listen to your music,' I informed him. 'Not *all* of it,' I added hastily, 'just a bit. You know. Have you got anything short? A *Moment Musicaux* sort of thing.'

'*Moment musical*,' corrected Van Dyke, who, he

informed me, had often been mistaken for a French-
man in the days when he lived in France. They
couldn't have seen him doing his Swedish drill, that's
all I can say.

The trouble with Van Dyke's music apparently
was that it was very difficult – so difficult, many
musicians had retired hurt in pursuit of it. A trum-
peter had fainted once in an attempt to do justice to
one of Van Dyke's acrobatic cadenzas.

'Ah,' Van Dyke had said, 'perhaps we need two
trumpets.' But even then, I gather, both trumpeters
had felt slightly sick. Serve them right for playing the
trumpet, I reckon. There can't be an instrument
anywhere of such naked egocentricity. Not that I
don't dissolve in tears whenever I hear them nicely
integrated into a Northern brass band, playing a
sentimental old Victorian song.

I wasn't expecting anything like a sentimental old
Victorian song from Van Dyke, though, given the
rigour and austerity of his intellectual inclinations.
When I curled up with Coleridge – or, even more
hallucinatory, the Pingouin wool pattern book – Van
Dyke was usually sitting up rather straight reading
Wholeness and the Implicate Order. What a terrifying
title, I ask you. I think I could have managed it if there
had been a concession to weakness in one direction at
least. *Boffo the Bear and the Implicate Order*, for
example. Or *Wholeness and Murder in Montmartre*.
But as it was, I could only stare in fascination at the
cover and wonder at the kaleidoscopic variety of the
human mind.

So. Would Van Dyke's work prove, as I suspected,
to be spiky, angular and not a little severe? I
surrounded myself with large floor cushions as he
fiddled with the record player.

'Thijs is a piece of mine called *Huantan*,' he
informed me. 'It ijs played by the Radio Wind
Ensemble conducted by Hans Vonk.'

Huantan? I thought that was a kind of soup. Hey, what sort of a guy was this? He calls his music after *soup*? Isn't that rather asking for smart-ass comments from philistines like myself?

'I thought the tubers were a little loud in the Leek and Potato.'

'And there was far too much vibrato in the tomato.'

I braced myself and waited.

Huantan began like a brass band exploding gently in deep space among the frosty stars. Comets whizzed past, walls of golden sound unfolded: crazy trains whirled into a vortex. Flowers opened and streamed by in the dark. Birds wheeled upwards on great thermals of sound as we gradually sank through layers of air towards cities, jungles, oceans.

Wait! Weren't we – yes – *underwater* now, and didn't millions of silvery fish thread needles of light through the brown swirls of water, and wasn't that – surely – the ghost of a giant, wrecked organ sounding somewhere among the eddies and currents and bobbing curls of weed? Weren't we, in fact, on the floor of the South China Sea?

Suddenly the organ spoke from its bed of sand; boomed, and rose gleaming and dripping towards the light, with fish and weeds dropping off it in a hubbub of aquatic alarm. I'm not sure what happened to the organ in the end, but I have a feeling when it re-entered the atmosphere it dissolved into sea breezes and oceanic calm. Also as the picture faded, I have to record that a squid farted. Well! All that for the price of an LP! No hangover, and it was all perfectly legal, too. I was speechless, and could only wring Van Dyke's hand as he had recently wrung my heart.

'Ja,' he concurred. 'I like this piece, too. Also the Radio Wind Ensemble are very good boys.'

I sat through *Huantan* once again, right away, and emerged even happier and convinced of one thing. Anyone who could write soup like that deserved a tranquil domestic life in order to devote himself to the main dish and, in due course, the desserts of a serene old age.

We booked the Register Office at Hackney Town Hall. It was a bit like getting married in Moscow only a lot less stylish. Van Dyke had made a trip to Swansea to get specially kitted out for the occasion.

'I need a wedding dress,' he explained to the mystified assistant. 'But I want it quite simple, so I can wear it afterwards as an ordinary dress.'

'*Suit!*' I hissed, *sotto voce.*

'Soup?' he asked, bemused but consistent.

Van Dyke's wedding suit was blue. It matched his eyes and the sky. A chilly wind blew but it was 21 March: the first day of spring. Blue birds were buccaneering against a British sky, and one was also perched artfully on my hat. I had sewn it there. My dress was blue and old and familiar, but my hat was new: a pillbox with veil, just like in the movies. So I sewed this bird to it. Not a real bird, I hasten to add. An artificial one, made out of feathers. But wait a minute – isn't there something Frankenstein-like about a bird made out of feathers? I suppose so. But then, there's something pretty monstrous about a wife made out of me.

By some quirk of fate I had to do a radio interview for the *Bookshelf* programme that same morning, to coincide with the launch of my first novel. Radio always terrifies me – it's the invisibility of it all, like radioactivity, but Hunter Davies was wearing corduroy trousers and that always has a soothing effect. Was I, he inquired, under thirty-five? Because if I was I might be eligible for a certain literary prize. You've guessed it: I was not. Why can't they have prizes for promising old newcomers?

Crackling with radioactivity, I leapt into a taxi outside Broadcasting House and sped towards Hackney. There on the Town Hall steps was Van Dyke waiting with our two friends who were to act as witnesses. He was a witty American saxophone player of Polish-Irish extraction. She, my most beautiful friend, was a potter and yoga teacher. All in all it was pretty alternative. If we'd thought of it in time we might have applied for an Arts Council grant to pay for the wedding.

These friends of ours had in a way been responsible for Van Dyke and myself becoming acquainted several years before, so it was only fair now that they should stand by us and face the music. Only there wasn't any music. The saxophone player was scratching himself quite rhythmically, our cats having set off his allergy, but that was all. This was to be the ceremony without any ceremony.

We were ushered into a strange dingy room. I felt that any minute the magistrate would come in and sentence us to matrimony – a life term. I didn't feel nervous, having used up all my adrenalin on the radio interview, and Van Dyke didn't look nervous either. But then, he'd been through all this before, years and years ago. As far as marriage was concerned we were both distinctly shopsoiled. We couldn't even claim to be promising old newcomers.

The door opened a crack and a strange supercilious smile sidled round it, followed by its owner. He was a man who walked sideways, leaning slightly to the left and somewhat twisted like the spire of Chesterfield Church. I think this was not so much a physical handicap as an affectation, designed to increase his dignity vicarwards. If he couldn't be a vicar at least he'd have a damn good try at being a church. The smile never faltered. He was doing his best to dispel the slightly funereal atmosphere.

He reminded us of the rather sinister origins of the institution of marriage, its supposed function and the behaviour that would be expected of us. But it was too late now to run away. The saxophone player scratched himself loudly in the stillness. The Registrar's smile swooped and gleamed in a snaky kind of way, culminating in a serpentine leer of triumph as he pronounced us man and wife. Or, as I'm sure we should have stipulated, woman and husband. He informed us with a lubricious glint that we were now permitted to exchange a kiss. We managed, somehow, though it seemed like the least appropriate setting for such a salutation.

From then on things started to improve. We went off to a Tandoori restaurant and ate a lot of fiery food. Then we decided to go for a trip on the river, and raced Thameswards only to discover that we'd just missed the last boat. So instead we went to see Woody Allen's film *Zelig*. I think *zelig* means happy in Jewish, so it seemed quite appropriate. Van Dyke slept through the entire performance. He didn't miss much. It was not one of Woody Allen's best. It was all sepia-toned as if it had all taken place decades ago. In fact, life in general was beginning to take on this quality.

Then it was back to my London house: sold, but not yet quite transferred. Nearly all my things had been packed up to go into store until we found somewhere to live. We finished the last bits of packing and then fell into bed, consumed not with lust but dust. Well, we were married. Our parents had all thrown up their hands in despair at our mad impetuous act. But it didn't feel so madly impetuous from where we were: prone with exhaustion.

'It is strange,' observed Van Dyke. 'Ij am old enough to be a grandfather, but my parents are still afraid I will do stupid like a young boy.'

Aar u suur u knowe wat u aar doing? Van Dyke Senior had written in his immaculate copperplate. A very good question. Of course we didn't. I suppose that's the main difference between their generation and ours. They knew what they were doing even

51

when they were twenty. We probably never will.

'You know, it's odd,' I mused. 'Our parents had long courtships, a stable environment, and marriages that lasted. When we were growing up we wanted to overturn all that. But now maybe we're trying to get back to that sort of stability. What do you think?'

Van Dyke did not answer. He was asleep. We had, it seemed, in some final way, joined our ancestors.

Chapter 6

Back in South Wales, the house-hunting resumed in earnest. We waited to hear from the West Country estate agents I had rung. Soon our hallway was piled high with information. Photos of jewel-like Cotswold cottages winked out at us from beneath bowers of roses.

'Look at this! Isn't it enchanting! Oh dear, it's seventy-five thousand.'

'And has only two bedroems. It would not be nearlij big enough for my piano—'

'Yes, yes! All right! But if it had only been three times as big and half the price, it would have been perfect!' I gazed longingly at the photographs of Cotswold roses. Early spring had come to our Welsh backyard, and the rusty scrap iron and builders' debris were noticeably not even in bud. How I missed Madame Gregoire Staechlin, Mrs Herbert Stevens, Madame Isaac Perière, and Madame Albert Carrière, the old bag! When would we be able to get together again for a *fin de siècle* coffee morning? (With Sapphic overtones, especially if Mrs Sam McGredy turned up with her vigorous habit and fiery hues.)

Eventually a real possibility emerged from the

welter of Fabergé cottages. The place in question was (now control yourself!) *Apple Tree Cottage*. It had, apparently, a very large attic, big enough for pianos. We approached it with fingers, toes and eyes crossed. It had been uninhabited for a few months, for it was owned by a Mr Fox, whose ancestry was more East End than Cotswold. Mr Fox was that most dangerous form of wild life, the speculative builder. He appeared to be building a bungalow in most of Apple Tree Cottage's garden.

'My word is my bond,' he said, leading us through the low, cottagey ground floor. 'There is a slight smell of damp in here, all right, I admit it straight away, but you can see as well as I can, there's no damp here, it's just that the house hasn't been lived in all winter. A couple of days with the heating on and that smell will disappear, believe you me, trust me, my word is my bond, you can't say fairer than that.'

I was experiencing a strangely schizophrenic sensation. One part of me – let's call it the spoilsport – couldn't help noticing that in the upper rooms the floors bounced slightly as we walked, and crossing the landing, the floorboards beneath my feet crumbled like a particularly delicious school pudding (I was raised in the days when we had school pudding. Nowadays, of course, we hardly even have schools).

The other part of me – let's call it the romantic fool – whispered encouragement. 'Of course the floors are springy! They're so deliciously ooooold! So what if the floorboards crumble? It can be fixed! And look at that lovely view of the dear little garden. If you close your left eye you can't see the new bungalow at all!'

Mr Fox led us to the top floor – a truly enormous barn-like space. You could have got four grand pianos up there, fitted them with motors, and had a Grand Prix. There was the problem of getting the pianos up the narrow cottagey staircase, of course. 'Never mind that!' cried the romantic fool. 'We can take the roof off! All you'll need is a crowbar and a block and tackle! I could do it myself before breakfast!'

'Oh, what a lovely room!' I burst out.

'Perfekt for my workroom,' agreed Van Dyke.

'Yes, you've got two million square feet of space here, easy,' said Mr Fox. 'As you can see, though I say it myself, it's a bargain, really and truly. You can't say fairer than that. I'm robbing myself, you can see that. A young couple came round here this morning and they practically put down a deposit on the spot. I'm telling you this as a friend, Mr Van Dyke – it's only fair you should know. I'm not in this for the money, you see. This transaction is nothing to me. What it is is, I've got too many projects on my hands. So it has to go. The wife loved it. We did think of moving in here ourselves, but, well, you now how it is. I've got too much on my hands.'

I noticed that the mighty beams were pitted with tiny holes. The spoilsport in me reared its ugly head.

'Is there woodworm?'

'I can tell you categorically from me, hand on heart, there is no live woodworm in this entire building,' intoned Mr Fox sepulchrally. 'What you see here is dead holes. If I'd have seen live wood-worm I'd have treated it, the work of a moment, no sweat. You need have no fears on that score, Mr Van Dyke. My word is my bond. Believe me, you have my word for it.' A patter of light dust fell onto his shoulders.

We skipped to our car and drove off in the grip of a rising hysteria. Van Dyke had, on this occasion, also succumbed to the romantic idiocy. 'It is fantastiek!' he cried. 'There is even roem for—' 'And think how lovely and old it is!' I drooled. 'Mr Fox said four hundred years at least!' Clever Mr Fox. How well he understood us. For a few weeks I dreamed of ancient floorboards, tiny cottage windows, and the garden.

55

Ah, the garden! All right, so it was north facing, about the size of an average bathroom, and shaded by a giant ash tree. Surely there was still room for a rose garden, a vegetable garden, an orchard, and an avenue of pleached hornbeams culminating in a statue of Diana the Huntress?

Soon the Building Society, to whom we had applied for a loan, sent their surveyor off to cast a cold eye on all this glory. And just as Mr Fox had understood us, the Building Society understood Mr Fox. They pointed out that Apple Tree Cottage was only slightly less damp than the North Sea; they drew our attention to the sinister dancing floor, the rotting boards, the worm-infested beams, and the fact that the porch had become detached from the house and was heading off up the hill by itself – a fact which had escaped our notice. They mentioned the bungalow in the garden, and the lack of a kitchen. (Crumbs! That's right! There *wasn't*!) They were prepared to lend us some money towards the purchase. But only enough to buy, as it were, a particularly delicious ice cream.

'The beasts!' I wept. 'We've lost it!'

Mr Fox was most upset. 'This is what you get with these Building Societies, you see, frankly what they're saying is utter rubbish, they're only interested in modern properties, this is simply really and truly not their sort of property. All right, I admit, there's one or two things that want putting right, and I've never said any different, you know me, and I'm quite prepared to do this for you, Mr Van Dyke, this has always been on the cards, and as to the financial side, I'm sure I can fix you upon that score to your satisfaction, my good name has always held me in good stead.'

We decided to start looking again, in Somerset. The cottages down there weren't quite so outrageously sexy, and we might, therefore, get more for our

– or rather, *their* – money. So off we went to the pink earth, the airy skies, and the Brendon Hills. We might not even have to buy a house this time, because I knew a dear old lady there who had said I could rent the cottage next door to hers. So I took Van Dyke down there, praying for him to be as ravished as I had been by the little white cottage by the rushing stream, the hanging woods and the red earth, which turned everything pink: even the sheep.

'Oh, look! There's the Quantocks!' I cried in rapture.

'Who? Friends of yours?' he inquired, braking suddenly and smiling obligingly at the nearest yokels. Yes, we were still having the occasional failure of communication. Like all Dutchmen, he spoke English much better than I did, but the thorny question of idiom was a real difficulty. When my mother asked him if he was peckish, he wasn't at all sure whether he was or not. Sometimes it was touch and go. ('Touch aand goe?')

'Look at the red earth! Isn't the garden lovely! Oh, my God, how marvellous: there's a bird!'

Van Dyke looked instead at the inside of the cottage, with a careful Dutch measuring sort of look which made my blood run cold. 'Excuse me, but whejre is my graand piano goijng to goe?' I saw his point. The cottage was two up, two down, and even a quite pixie-ish couple would have to take it in turns to yawn and stretch. It was clear that any grand piano would have to have at least one leg permanently in the garden. In fact, we'd probably have more room if we lived in the grand piano itself.

'Aand if we haav a babje, we will need even moer roem.'

'Oh, I don't know. Babies aren't very big, are they? It could go under the grand piano.' I could see I was beat, though.

Van Dyke very cleverly took me off to a dear little harbour town called Watchet, from which, I discovered, the Ancient Mariner had set sail. Here we had fish and chips. Van Dyke soon discovered that a mixture of chips and literary associations could rouse me from the deepest depression.

'Never mind,' I chirped, already up to the hairline in salt and vinegar, 'it was much too small, you're right.'

'I get klaustrophobia onder such low ceilings.'

'Yes. So do I. Besides, I bet it's miles from the nearest Safeway's.'

So . . . where were we going to live? I was already getting quite attached to the chip shop, but even I could see that there wasn't nearly enough room for the grand piano – unless it was filleted, that is. Not a bad idea, in fact. You'd get eight octaves of fish fingers, for a start. 'C Bass and chips, please, and make it allegretto!'

Since we were in Watchet we dropped into the local estate agent's, just to have a look. It's a habit that's hard to shake off even after you've found your house and completed your move. Like married men eyeing up other women, I still cast half-interested looks into estate agents' windows. And on this occasion what did we see but the House of our Wildest Dreams. Yes, again.

It was a huge rambling place, with a seventeenth-century back part which had once been (get this) a *sea captain's cottage*, and a most elegant early eighteenth-century front with the original Queen Anne windows, shutters, fireplaces, alcoves, mouldings, dados, ha-has and doo-dahs. Admittedly, the present inhabitants had made a few changes. The attic rooms were full of old mattresses: the outbuilding (our potential Granny annexe) piled high with bits of old railway carriages and plates of raw meat.

If you're breeding deerhounds, of course, you do need a fair amount of meat. You also need a place for them to run about, and that, no doubt, was why they had concreted over the entire back garden and strung up lots of chainlink fencing. But what of that? The romantic fool was back in the driving seat. 'Never mind that concrete,' she whispered. 'A morning with a hammer and chisel and that'll all be gone. And look at those lovely high walls! Yes, a walled garden! Wouldn't Madame Gregoire look glorious sprawling up there? Listen to the seagulls! And just think: you're only twenty seconds' walk from the fish-and-chip shop.'

We did notice that the roof appeared to be covered with a tarpaulin and kind of glued down, but the vendor, a charming lady who spent most of her time running after the deerhounds with a shovel assured us that the tarpaulined roof was quite common in the area. 'We couldn't afford to have it done properly,' she said. But I'm sure that was just a figure of speech.

We took a last, feverish look at the house and drove away, speechless with longing. I drew several detailed plans transforming the garden from a waste of concrete and chainlink fencing to something little short of Versailles. In my mind's eye I saw the theoretical baby toddling by the sea. It was all so painfully exciting that we couldn't sleep properly for weeks.

The Building Society's surveyor found it exciting, too. So exciting that he took one look at the tarpaulined roof and ran back to his car, cringing all the way. The Building Society said sorry, they couldn't lend us the price of a single roof tile this time, but they had deferred their usual survey fee and were only charging us £14. (I wish I were a surveyor, don't you? Running back to your car at £28 a minute seems like pretty good money to me.)

We were heartbroken. Like disappointed lovers, we vowed never to look at another house again, but to live, instead, like Diogenes, in a barrel. When we visited my parents in Gloucestershire, and they suggested we look at a couple of houses in the nearby town, we couldn't summon the emotional energy. But we went off, all the same, to be polite. This time, though, we were looking at Victorian semis, not rural ruins. The first house left us cold. The second was all wrong. But the third . . .

Ah, the third. Though I had vowed never again to fall in love with a house, one glimpse of its manly, jutting gables was enough. While it was clearly mortgageable, it was also full of Gothic grandeur.

Well, when I say *grandeur*, it *is* only a four-bedroomed semi. The sort of place Dracula might well have retired to when the Biting had to Stop. Surrounded by deep gloomy evergreens, crowned by beetling gables (and when I say *beetling* . . . but more of that anon), it boasted long rusting Transylvanian window latches, and not just mullions but *crumbling* mullions. The great thing about limestone is that it falls to bits so quickly. You don't need gales. Just a few sparrows fluttering up and down around the façade for a year or two, and, my dear, the limestone simply *drops off* in great flakes leaving the whole house with that pitted-by-Civil-War-cannonballs look, even if it was only built in 1906.

Enraptured by the exterior, we crossed the threshold and negotiated the dank flagstones of the hall. Dank flagstones! Imagine! One expected at any moment to see the satanic shade of young Laurence Olivier glide past, wild-eyed, muttering *Rebecca!* or *Cathy!* in an anguished undertone. Within the house was the Heart of Darkness. The Arts and Crafts builders of 1906, who had adorned it with built-in dressers and Art Nouveau fireplaces, had apparently forgotten about windows. The present occupant had reacted to the pervasive gloom by painting the rooms toad brown, slime green, varicose blue and black. On the principle, I suppose, that if you can't beat it you may as well join it.

We fumbled our way around in the dark ('This

wall feels quite nice, darling ... darling?'). We
bruised ourselves on delightful architectural details.
And best of all, we failed to perceive any serious
structural defects. In fact, we failed to perceive
anything at all except the wonderful Gothic atmosphere.

By the time we blinked our way into the sunshine
outside the back door, we were fatally enchanted. *Do
Go Up the Garden*, encouraged the vendor, and so we
set off, though it soon became clear we were fatally
ill-equipped without crampons and oxygen cylin-
ders. But we did not notice the Himalayan gradient,
nor the lack of shed, greenhouse, garage, or even,
dammit, path. This was because the lavender was out
and great murmurations of bees hung about us. *O the
lavender! O the bees!* was the order of the day.

From the top of the garden we gazed down,
panting, upon the house, and anyone with any sense
would have taken this opportunity of noticing the
missing tiles, the cracked roof-verges, and the tottering chimneys. We, of course, gazed beyond these
trivial details to the blue hills. *O the hills!* I cried. This
was IT. I felt it in my bones. Third time lucky. We
duly applied to the Building Society. This time,
surely, they would come up with the goods. After all,
it was a suburban semi. What more did they want?

The Building Society was, of course, outrageously
rude about Romantic No. 21. They demanded that we
root out the rot, scoop up the slime and, worst of all,
shoot the woodworm. 'Isn't there room for us and the
woodworm in God's creation?' I wailed. But apart
from demanding a long list of repairs, they did appear
to be willing, thank God, to push the necessary cash
our way. No. 21 was all but ours. Immediately I began
to feel deeply attached to South Wales. The dear
builders' yard at the back! Who would take care of it?
Would it feel lonely?

No. 21 wasn't really what we had expected to end

up with: a suburban semi in a small town. But as suburban semis go, it *was* the nearest thing to Elsinore. What's more, though the town (Stroud) was a town, it wasn't much of a town. Up at our end the pavements get a bit half-hearted and the trees get more arrogant. Besides, it did strike us as convenient that it was only a few minutes' walk from the bank, the post office, and – to be fearlessly frank and honest – the Maternity Hospital.

Chapter 7

It's a well-known fact that the Older Woman has difficulty getting pregnant. I had been the Older Woman since I was twenty-seven, when a bitch on the beauty counter offered me a face cream 'for the older skin'. In fact, I'd been even older at sixteen, in my twinset and pearls. I'd looked fifty-eight, and still have the passport photos to prove it. I've never looked young, or felt young, even when I actually *was* and especially then. Dear me, it's such a grimly serious business, being young. You spend all your time trying to work out the meaning of life, and all your body wants to do is have babies.

Then, once you're old and grey and full of sleep, you give up trying to work out the meaning of life, and decide at the last moment to have a baby. By then, of course, your body has lost interest in the whole thing, and is instead cultivating an antique gleam like a piece of valuable furniture. It does not wish to be hauled, suddenly, into maternity, thank you very much. By now what the body would like is the life style of an Abbess: a succession of austere pleasures. A little gardening before Compline: couple of hours' Illuminating before Confession.

So it's no wonder Older Women take ages to get pregnant. (What a horrible word pregnant is, by the way. It sounds like pigs snorting. I shall substitute 'with child'.) I looked forward to the rituals, ancient and modern. I would spend the night on country hillsides when the moon was full, sleeping where the magicky herbs grew. (I hoped it didn't matter that Van Dyke would be two miles away down the valley tucked up in the nearest inn. He has such a horror of draughts.) If that didn't work, I'd try hedgehogs under the bed, keys suspended from the ceiling, and the thighbone of a frog strapped to my left knee.

Nor would I scorn the advice of modern science. I would take my temperature every morning to see how I compared to Rome, Riyadh and Rio de Janiero. I would abstain from drugs, alcohol, tea, coffee, aspirins and horse-riding just in case.

I visited my London doctor. He had the silvery polished look of a very distinguished conjuror, a member of the Magic Circle. And deft! My word! He can remove what needs to be removed from your body as gently as a feather leaving a velvet cushion on a light breeze. Now you see it, now you don't and Abracadabra! Ladies and Gentlemen . . . it has turned into a flock of doves.

My doctor was another reason why I hated to leave London. Once you've found a doctor like that, no one else will do. It's the same with hairdressers. Take José of Stoke Newington: seven snips of his magic scissors and you look not only thirty years younger, but solvent and optimistic. These men are touched with genius and in any civilized country would be Dukes or Earls by now.

My doctor waved me off amicably on my mission, beaming as only a benign grandfather can at the prospect of another bluestocking rescued for motherhood. He had rendered me, apparently, as fertile as the River Po. It must be delightful to live

64

in the Po valley, don't you think?

'Good Heavens!' your visitors cry. 'Your corn is as high as an elephant's eye!'

'Ah, well,' you shrug, 'every spring the Po over-flows all over our vegetable patch.'

As the train carried me back to South Wales, images of Mediterranean fertility alternated with terrifying glimpses of imagined parenthood. A baby cried on the train. Thank God it wasn't mine. And it suddenly struck me: what if you and your baby are on a train alone, and you wish to go to the loo? How in the world do you perform this simple function? Do you dangle the baby from your teeth the while? The mind boggled – and so, all too soon, would the body.

'Hello! How did it go? Wouljd you like a cup ov tea?' inquired Van Dyke.

'Not now! I've got a headache! You men are all the same: only after one thing!' I hissed, and ran off upstairs to lock myself in my room. I composed myself to composition and listened to some Gregorian chant. I sensed the Abbess' last stand. Down below in the water meadow the bullocks were dashing about in a maddened sort of way. Spring was sharpening its claws. I could hear the thunder of history at my door.

'Ijt is only me, with a cup of cocoa.'

'Leave it on the landing: I'm in the middle of something tricky.'

I was in the middle of sheer terror, and believe me, that's tricky.

Leaving London had been bad enough. But one could live without it. So I had exchanged the Hub of the Universe for a muddy field and a rocky outcrop. So what? There was a certain Chinese satisfaction to be gained from these simplicities. The philosopher Su-Lim was exiled to the rocky outcrop, in the time of the Empress of Iron, Tha-Cha. For nine years the philsopher meditated on the Meaning of Life. In the tenth year she came down from rocky outcrop and said, 'You who seek to know the meaning of life I say, first sweep the hearth stone.'

Terrific stuff, all that. It would make great street theatre with a couple of tambourines, bare feet, and a nose flute. You'd be into really big money. You'd be talking telephone numbers. There's nothing the fat capitalists of the West like more than a dose of that swept-clean Chinese purity. So the austerities of exile were doing me good. The rocks and rivers sharpened up my sense of what I valued most in life: silence, space and freedom. Those measureless treasure houses. But what happens to silence, space and freedom, my friends, when a baby looms? What happens to the big three then?

I trembled to think. All my prejudices rose and blanketed me like a fog. I couldn't see a single reason why a baby would be a good idea. All I could see were the 1,001 reasons why I'd remained childless up till now. Wasn't I the worst person in the world to contemplate such a thing? (A conviction shared by all my friends – 'What, *you*?' they choroused amid gales of mirth. 'The very *idea*!')

I was so scared that my heart was fluttering about like a moth with claustrophobia. And that was another thing. Apart from my constitutional irresponsibility, my history of fickle and feckless escapes and my fear and loathing of children, there was my poor clapped-out old body to consider. How could I be so reckless as to deliver it into maternity? Not to mention delivering the baby into – and out of – it.

Even newborn babies weigh about seven pounds, don't they? Seven pounds! That's fourteen packs of butter for goodness' sake! Just the thought of trying to carry that much butter about was enough to give me a hernia. My wrists were weak: my migraines almost continuous, my veins varicose and my belly bellicose. My spine had long since gone for ever and my fingernails were visibly disappearing at that very moment. Yes! There went the last thumbnail! It hit the windowpane with a plaintive ping. (I tend, when in great anguish, to bite them off and flick them about.) If I was in this bad shape now, what would be left of me after nine months of with childhood? I couldn't bear to think about it.

What next? Life had to go on. But I was damned sure I wasn't going to let it get above itself, let alone start renewing itself all over the place.

'Ijt is a lovely day,' observed Van Dyke. 'Why don't we goe for a pijc-nijc in the woods?'

'Not the woods!' I shrieked in panic. 'Why don't we go for a picnic in ... er ... the supermarket?'

Surely I'd be safe in the supermarket. Surely nobody ever got pregnant there. I hung about quite determinedly in the supermarket that spring. I tried to avoid the most remote and romantic corners of it, of course: the wine and spirits department, for example, was quite dangerously secluded. But I reckoned if I kept moving and bared my teeth and spat in the faces of all male persons, I ought to be all right. Although you can never tell with some male persons. That might be just the very thing to get them going.

When Van Dyke managed to drag me away from the shops and Neath bus station (where I whiled away many a happy hour studying the timetables), I condescended to go for walks along the most exposed cliffs of the Gower Peninsula. The weather was fine, but I wore huge sacklike old jerseys and great baggy trousers left over from the British in India. I stopped having baths, washing my hair, or cleaning my teeth. I became grotesquely unattractive, even by my standards. Before long I could hardly bear to sleep with myself. I only hoped it would have a similar effect on Van Dyke.

I reckoned I was doing pretty well. But nature was being fairly provocative all over the place. Even the lowest and most repulsive forms of life were busily reproducing themselves. One had to fight one's way through clouds of pollen and showers of blossom just to get to the post office. The air was thronged with nest-building, egg-laying birds. The fields were positively congested with leaping lambs; the rivers boiling with fishlets and ducklets, and the walls were slippery with sluglets.

Walking along a high Roman road one day in an effort to escape, by sheer altitude, all the reckless seeding and breeding going on in the valleys, we came across an appalling sight: a great dollop of frogspawn, as big as a cartwheel, and isolated in the midst of rocks and grass, in what was presumably a dried-out puddle. Thousands of little black eyes of life lay there watching us, it seemed, with desperation. *Don't let us dry out!* they seemed to plead.

But what could we do? We were ill-equipped to embark on a tadpole-bussing service. You try and pick up a handful of frogspawn one day. Even if you can conquer your revulsion, the wretched stuff just slips away in strings. So we did nothing – yet. Back down in Clwch we had lunch, and then I got out the two sturdiest plastic carrier bags I could find and a tablespoon with *Newnham College* engraved on the handle. The spoon intended to ladle out Toad-in-the-Hole to starving bluestockings had a nobler destiny in store. It was to rescue the frogspawn-in-a-jam.

I want it to be recorded that, frivolous and worthless as my life no doubt seems to the impartial observer, that hill was very steep by British standards. Even though I was, for me, fairly fit at the time, I had to stop twice to put out the fire in my throat. At last I got to the top, and there, sure enough, was the wretched frogspawn: still stupidly stuck in the driest place for miles. With all the authority of a Newnham College dinner lady I shovelled it into my carrier bags. It lurched in in great out-of-control quivers.

68

Then, a full carrier bag in each hand, I stood up. And very nearly *broke my spine*.

Have you any idea what frogspawn weighs? What on earth do they put in it? I suppose all that jelly is packed with nutrition. After all, it has to keep them going for three weeks while they grow tails, doesn't it? Suppose I had a potential 500 frogs in my bag – that seems a modest enough estimate. Three meals a day for three weeks . . . that would be over 36,000 frog dinners, not counting cocoa and biscuits at bedtime. No wonder I staggered along screaming with pain, looking to right and left for water, Pepsi Cola, anything. Not for me, you understand – for *them*.

I didn't care if it had saccharine in it, effluent in it, or wild Welsh crocodiles in it. Let them take their chances. What had any of them ever done for me? Would they bother to write to me when they went off to college? Would they remember my birthday? Would they heck. As soon as their damned tails dropped off they'd be over the horizon and that's the last I'd ever see of them until they needed money.

'Right, you lot!' I had spotted a brackish pool. I emptied my bags into it, and the lump of jelly which had been so awful on land instantly sank, steadied itself, expanded and became a beautiful underwater gallery-nursery. All the little black eyes of life became dimmed beneath the green slime; safer, surely, from the beaks and teeth that would seek them out.

'Goodbye!' I cried. 'Be good. And never go anywhere with a stranger.' But were they listening? Of course not.

Back home, when I washed out the carrier bags, I found one solitary black dot of frogspawn clinging to a corner.

'Dammit!' I cried. 'You'll be the death of me! Why can't you be like the other kids?'

I pulled my boots back on and trudged across the heaving, seedstruck earth to the stream. I found a bit of backwater and released my last blob of life into it.

'Go forth,' I instructed it, 'but for God's sake don't multiply.' As I stomped back home, braving the bullocks, I reckoned I'd done my bit for motherhood.

'Are you completely maaad?' asked Van Dyke. But soon there were more interesting questions to be asked.

In the good old days, what you got was an angel. You can see it in all the paintings. There's Mary, deep into her novel, and you can tell she's just got to the bit where the plot thickens so fast they must have added an egg when POW! Ker-ZAM! This good-looking surfer with wings lands on her windowsill. 'Dear oh dear,' she's thinking, 'I do wish this flat wasn't so near the airport,' when the air clears and the surfer waves a lily at her (he's somehow terribly San Francisco), and says, 'Hi Mary how are you today? Listen honey, I'm from Madonna Laboratories Inc., and this is a singing pregnancy test results service. It's positive, sweetheart, so have a nice day! Alleluia Alleluia Alleluia.' And then he flaps off looking beatific. Angels! I've had them up to here! They wouldn't look so beatific if it was them that got pregnant.

That kind of service, however, is no longer available in modern Britain. But then, what is? You have to do the whole thing yourself nowadays, starting with buying the lipstick. So this is why I found myself hesitating over a chemist's counter in South Wales trying to weigh up the Best Buy as far as Pregnancy Testing Kits were concerned.

It was quite a task. They were all so expensively packaged they might have been mini-computers. The boxes had that grey and white beautifully under-stated classics-of-modern-art look that you often get with products which are faintly obscene. I chose the most stylish, paid a large amount of money, and ran off into the hills. Inside the designer box was the designer device. It seemed like sacrilege to let any of

70

one's bodily fluids anywhere near it. But that seemed to be what was required.

I got up at 6 a.m. and did the deed. The bathroom was filled with sunlight and I felt fairly optimistic that this would all prove to be a silly false alarm. I had to wait two hours for the result, so I put the modern Italian micro-sculpture of perspex and metal on the windowsill complete with its two drops of pee, and went back to bed.

In bed I dreamed of starting up an old-fashioned pregnancy testing service for people depressed and alienated by all this metal and perspex. Nostradamus, I'd call it, after the Renaissance astrologer. What you'd get for your £99.95 would be an original parchment scroll with an individual prediction upon it, such as:

In the sixth sestiad about 1985
A babe will be born who will probably thrive
Wars, fires, plagues and flying machines
Will give his poor mum the most horrible dreams
An emperor will come out of the West
And raise the prices of babies' vests
CAPITALISM this will be called
And all who suffer it will be slightly appalled
But the babe will grow tall, lie in bed until noon
Smoke, drink and leave home not a moment too
soon.

Crumbs! It was 8 a.m. The sun was quite fierce by now, lying in hot patches on the bedroom carpet, but Van Dyke was still sleeping like a baby. Or that's how I thought of it, in my ignorance. I was soon to learn that anyone still asleep by 8 a.m. is certainly not sleeping like a baby.

I nipped to the bathroom (I could still *nip* in those days) and peeped at the silver and perspex sculpture. Good God! It had grown a sort of rusty brown circle,

71

like a bad-tempered sun rising on an immaculate landscape. The Ring! I was seized by a Wagnerian wave of shock. This was, I knew, the tell-tale sign of that most impossible thing: a positive result. What, me? With child? *Me?*

The top of my life seemed to blow off and a lot of unearthly light came bursting in. I sat down hard on the edge of the bath and watched bits of the bathroom wheel madly about in search of one another. I couldn't have been more amazed if the Archangel Gabriel himself had come surging up out of the loo in a wet-suit studded with diamonds. For a few minutes I tried to come to grips with the idea of motherhood in solitude. But what am I saying? In solitude? Not any more. Another life, albeit tadpolean, had seized its chance. And it was going to take more than a college spoon and a couple of carrier bags to get this one safely launched into the world.

Chapter 8

For a few days I sat at my desk and stared into space, trying to get my mind round the momentous concept. Everybody said that once a baby came life was never the same. It was easy to see what my life had consisted of up till now. Most of the day was spent sitting at a desk, writing. This was known – satirically, perhaps – as work. Then there was eating, drinking and sleeping. Any bits of time left over, the hours that used to be spent gardening, were now dedicated to hill walking. Trips to nightclubs and cinemas did not loom very large these days. With such a modest life style it didn't seem to me that my life was going to change all that much.

After all, newborn babies spent most of their time asleep, didn't they? I ran a quick mental video of what life might be like a year hence. I worked, the babe asleep in a basket under my desk. I ate, drank and slept – and so did the babe. We went for hill walks, the babe asleep in a sling on Van Dyke's back. I attacked my garden, with the babe dozing amongst the pots of geraniums. It all seemed pretty straightforward, really. I couldn't understand what all the fuss was about.

But then – what if it was a difficult one? What if it stayed awake all night, crying? What if it was ill? What if it crawled early – say, at four weeks? What if it didn't like us much? What if there was something wrong with it? Would I be able to love it? Fear seized my soul – and then practical panic set in as well. What would we need in terms of equipment? What would we have to do? How often would it need changing? Would once a day be enough? What did you do if it didn't stop crying? What if you dropped it? Oh, God! I couldn't get to grips with the idea at all. It was too huge. My mind was losing its elasticity. It was beginning to droop.

And so was my body. A deep fatigue set in, as if my shoes had been nailed to the ground. It was impossible to believe that a couple of weeks ago I had gone striding for miles along mountain tops carrying great bags of frogspawn. Now I could hardly walk to the kitchen carrying an empty tea cup. I couldn't do anything except sit and stare at the sunbeams. And even that was quite hard work.

Luckily there was nothing physical to do. By now our house-hunting was completed. All we had to do was sit and wait for all the legal processes to unfold, until we could move into our Draculean semi, or *Dunbitin'* as I liked to think of it. This waiting for the lawyers to do their stuff takes weeks and weeks. But what were weeks any more? What were months? The main task in hand was to get through – what was it called? – *breakfast*, without collapsing with whatsit? – *exhaustion*.

All my words seemed to have disappeared. But who needed words when grunts would do? My head had turned to stone, and it was impossible to contemplate anything more ambitious than a morning sunk in the armchair, gazing into nothingness like an Easter Island head. I was aware, however, of the need to make the odd gesture towards animation.

I would try to read a bit. Starting with the breakfast cereal packets and working my way up slowly through postcards to pamphlets. Van Dyke brought a lot of books home about How To Expect A Baby. The first day I looked at their covers. The next day, with a massive effort, I opened them and looked at the pictures. That was a big mistake – especially the pictures of the actual births. I started to read the books, in the end, to try and avoid looking at the pictures.

The books' accounts of pregnancy bore no relation to my experience. For a start, they all agreed that nausea would hang over me for the first three months. Well, there had been a moment in a Neath fish shop when the smell of raw fish had zoomed up my nostrils and paralyzed my brain and I had had to dash out into the fresh air before anything worse happened. But I wouldn't call it feeling sick so much as being fish-struck.

All the same, there was unanimity among the experts and, more alarmingly, among my friends, who all reported the first three months of their pregnancies as being something of a Vomitathon. Being sick is something of which I have an unnatural dread, since it has hardly ever happened to me. But I was stoically prepared to do my bit for nausea, if that was what was required.

I installed myself in the bathroom and waited. There were a lot of faded old Socialist newspapers in there – relics of Byron's former occupation – and I glanced casually at them when I could summon up the energy. Good Heavens! The things that were going on in the world! The exploitation and greed! It made one absolutely sick . . . Or *did* it?

I had to admit I did not feel at all sick. In fact, I was ravenous. If I hadn't been a vegetarian, I could have eaten a horse. As it was, I could have eaten a horse chestnut, complete with birds' nests and lost kites. I craved crackers. But could I summon up the energy to go downstairs and get some? Or should I just sit here and chew on some loo paper instead? After all, it had been a tree once. (Or, in the case of recycled loo paper, twice.)

I had to go downstairs. It was only an hour after breakfast, but already a rampaging hunger had me in its grip. I wanted bread! A couple of loaves at least! I wanted scrambled eggs on toast! I wanted it fast and I wanted it big! At night I even had to take banana sandwiches to bed with me to devour at 3 a.m. What on earth was going on? I'd heard of eating for two, but this was eating for two thousand.

A sudden froggy dread seized me. I'd always enjoyed lying in the bath: enjoyed it, perhaps, a little too much. Was there something deeply, atavistically amphibian in my genetic make-up? And had this Dutchman from the below-sea-level world of muddy dykes and webbed feet completed the vicious circle? Was I not so much with child as with frog? WRITER LAYS THOUSANDS OF EGGS IN RESERVOIR: FOUL PLAY SUSPECTED.

One has such strange thoughts when one is with child. I had no strange cravings, though. I just wanted to eat everything in sight. Especially the big soft brown cushions, which were looking increasingly like cinnamon buns. Even the books began to look rather delicious. I might as well eat them. After all, they were all wrong. They all warned that, what with the nausea, most pregnant women lost up to 14 lb in the first three months. Whereas my desperate hunger had led to such shameful gorging that I'd already put on all the weight I was entitled to in the whole pregnancy while the baby was still no bigger than a bean.

Although, how much weight *was* I entitled to? The books couldn't agree. One said 8 kg; another reckoned up to 50 lb was OK. But what were 8 kg or 50 lb in terms of real flab? 8 kg sounded like an air letter: 50 lb like a lorryload of coal. I tried to work out what it meant in good old British pounds, shillings and pence, and immediately my head began to reel. Avoid mental arithmetic if you are with child. It can lead to morning, afternoon and evening sickness.

Poised upon the scales, I tried to summon up the energy to be appalled at my weight gain. Then I dragged myself back to the books. What was my Fate to be, now that I'd got so fat? The books were unanimous: what awaited me was Oedema, Intertrigo and Pre-Eclampsia. Just the sound of them made me want to faint. But as yet they hadn't showed up. Maybe if I ate nothing but spinach for the next six months, I might be all right. I bit my nails in anxiety. But stop! How many calories were in a fingernail, for God's sake?

I hadn't made a very distinguished start. Stupor, torpor and insane greed did not fit in with the popular idea of pregnancy. Surely one was supposed to wander off through soft-focused fields of buttercups, the low sun turning one's hair to a golden halo? I pulled on my boots.

'What are you doijng?' inquired Van Dyke, finding me pale and panting from the effort.

'I'm going to wander through foft-socused fields of futtercups,' I sighed. ' I can't go on lounging about like this. I've got to get fit before it's too late.' I staggered to the door. I'd planned a walk that was downhill nearly all the way: down the field to the stream, along the path for 200 yards or so, then back along the road. Good heavens, it wasn't a walk at all, really. You could have done it leaving one leg at home, like a pair of compasses.

I got down to the stream all right. I even admired a wild yellow iris in bloom. Then I began to feel extremely strange. How did this walking business go, exactly? One foot after another, wasn't it? But where were my feet, dammit? One seemed to be sunk in a clump of bullrushes, the other up a tree somewhere. I sat down on a rotting stump for a rest, and waited for my sense of how to walk to return to me.

But, oh dear, now there was a new problem: how to get up off the rotting stump. It seemed I would sit there for ever like a garden gnome, in fossilized contemplation of the reeds and darting fish. How did they manage to go on darting like that? Were any of them pregnant? Would I ever be able to do anything, ever again? What on earth was the wretched baby up to in there, making me feel like this?

I suppose it was really a massive project, this withchildhood of mine. It was like buying a derelict medieval house and trying to turn it into a smart hotel and restaurant overnight. I could almost sense the frenzied activity within me, the cursing carpenters, the perplexed plumbers, as my hormones bustled about in desperation, struggling with the dry rot, the wet rot and the extreme fragility of the ancient structure. 'This is absurd,' I said eventually. 'Get up, you lazy old cow.'

I staggered to my feet and lumbered as far as the road. One bend and I'd be able to see our house. My bones had turned to lead and my muscles to water. I crashed sideways into the hedge. Our neighbours walked past. I tried to look as if I was meant to be in the hedge, my nose stuck in an empty Coca-Cola can.

'Good afternoon!' I cried with false *bonhomie* into the can. 'Terrific birds' nests along here.' They gave me strange looks and walked quickly past.

I de-hedged myself and got as far as the bend in the road. There was our house up ahead! Only about 25 million light years away! And thank heaven someone had put a seat down here at the roadside. I collapsed on to it. So it looked a bit strange, my sitting down on a seat twenty-five yards from my own front door. So what? I was eccentric. For all they knew, I had quarrelled with Van Dyke. Goodness knows I had cause enough.

'What have you done to me, O microscopic blob of life?' I wailed just as the neighbours came back around the corner. I improvised a song on the theme and trilled it casually.

> O tiny microscopic blob of life, blob of life,
> I went down Mississippi for to get myself a wife
> Singing tiny microscopic blob of life.

They smiled as they sidled past.

'Lovely day for a walk.' Cunning Welsh sadists.

I managed to do the last twenty-five yards in one mad rush. It was uphill, too. But it's amazing what you can do when you don't want to look too much of a fool in front of the neighbours. Only fools care about looking a fool in front of the neighbours, of course. I burst back into the house and fell headlong on to the cat.

'Oh, God, God!' I moaned ostentatiously – my way of getting Van Dyke to make me a cup of tea. Not ordinary tea: raspberry leaf tea, which was supposed to be good for pregnant women. It tasted of old barns but there was something reassuring about that. Van Dyke was halfway through a housing development for clarinet and flute, but he rushed obediently to the kettle. I reflected, as I lay there waiting for the ceiling to go back up above where it belonged, that we were beginning to get into a kind of routine.

'It says in this book,' pointed out Van Dyke, over our cups of old straw, 'that you shouldn't goe for walks if you don't feel like ijt.'

'Heavens! What a good idea! Why didn't I think of that before?'

This was immensely reassuring. From now on I would sit in my chair until it was time to move house. Then, after the move, I would sit in my chair in

Gloucestershire. The books said that you could even give birth sitting down these days: in something called a birthing chair, once popular in the eighteenth century and increasingly revived nowadays in the more fashionable maternity hospitals. Good-oh. I would be able, with any luck, to sit this one out.

Van Dyke was a little uneasy at the prospect of my turning back into a pumpkin. He proposed a project for me: I was to think of names. I sighed irritably. Think of names? Who did he think I was? An Olympic athlete? It seemed to me that I'd have to train for weeks just to be able to remember my own name, let alone invent ones for the yet unborn.

All the same, I could see he had a point. We had to have a name for it. In fact, we had to have two: one male, one female. It was quite a task, though. I still haven't managed, after five years, to think of a name for the cat. Boringly enough, she remains to this day mere Pussy. But clearly, for the Van Dykelet, mere Baby would not do.

I sat still and concentrated hard. Surely it would be easy enough to think of a name you liked. But it's a minefield of pretension. First of all, I discovered I had all sorts of snobbish prejudices about a whole genre of post-war, 100 per cent nylon names. Things like Sharon and Tracey and Gary. I found out later that they all dated back to the Persian Empire at least, but I still couldn't get terribly excited about them. Nor could I really believe in their antiquity. 'And then the godlike Odysseus turned to his companion, Gary—' No, no, it wouldn't do.

Robert Herrick, the seventeenth-century English poet, had had a pet spaniel called Tracie. And perhaps even Milton had had a guide dog called Sharon. Or – wait a minute – *Charon*! Dog-headed god (and try saying that after three pints of raspberry leaf tea) and guardian of the Underworld! Had this led Milton to his epic work? Ferried, in his imagination, between the worlds of the living and the dead, every time he crossed the road? Sit, Charon! Good Dog! Or should it be Good God?

But wait a minute. I was supposed to be thinking of names. These rogue outbursts of scholarly conjecture must be firmly shut away with the College spoon. It was Goodbye to All That. Today we play the name game. And there were some names I really liked: plain Old English names such as Henry, William, James, Anne, etc. But they had already been cornered by the Royal Family. I didn't want people to think I'd called my child after a princeling. (I am of course a closet Royalist, hiding my tears on the day of the Royal wedding behind a copy of the *New Left Review*.)

I didn't want my baby to have the same name as all the other babies. So a lot of quite pleasant possibilities such as Thomas, Benjamin, Sara and Hannah were out. But I realized it was a bit mean to land my offspring with a name that was outrageously unusual, drawn though I was to Lorenzo and Cleopatra. My teenage niece disagreed. She thought the name should be as unusual as possible. She knew people called things like China and Sky, and they were, apparently, *brilliant* names, their owners the envy of all their friends.

I was deeply tempted, for several weeks, to call the baby Forest. Everywhere I looked, all I could see was trees. They must have exercised some subliminal effect on the child's development. But Forest Van Dyke? Wasn't there a danger that with a name like that the government would want to build a motorway across the wretched child?

Other names had to be rejected because of their inescapable associations. I'd always loved the name Oliver, but wouldn't it lead straight to homosexuality and the antiques business? Not that I objected to homosexuality *per se* – it conveniently did away with the need for a daughter-in-law. But I did like the idea of grandchildren. Another name to conjure with was Max. Max Van Dyke sounded pretty snappy. Kind of Max von Sydow with pratfalls. But wouldn't anyone called Max inevitably hang around hotel lounges, smoking cigars and end up on a fraud charge?

Then, suddenly, like a blue arrow from heaven, the perfect names came whizzing into my head. Freddie and Poppy. Freddie was a clever name: apparently working class as in Fred, but secretly aristocratic as in Frederick. A perfectly democratic name. A name that pretended to be stupid. How clever! And not all that common, either.

As for Poppy: how could any girl called Poppy fail to turn out optimistic, lively and glowing? The name of a flower, but not all weedy and serious like Daphne or Laurel. A glorious, brave, blazing name. I ran into Van Dyke's study.

'I've got it!' I cried. 'Poppy and Freddie!' Van Dyke burst out in the most contemptuous laugh I have ever heard him utter, except at British food.

'Ijt is impossible!' he roared. 'In Holland, Freddie is always the name of a – what is ijt – con man. Ijt is the name of a crook.' I was dismayed.

'What about Poppy?'

'Poppy in Dutch is a name which means little doll. Ijt would be O.K. for a babje but not an older girl. It would sound sillje. Like Dollie.'

'All right!' I sulked. 'You choose the bloody name. It might as well have a Dutch name, anyway, to go with Van Bloody Dyke.'

Dutch names are odd. They usually have one long formal one, ending in -us and sounding like a medieval pope. This is the name that goes on documents: PETRUS, JOHANNES, JACOBUS. But they never actually get called it. They're all called by shortened forms, and believe me, you can't get any shorter than Dutch abbreviations. They're so energy-conscious they don't waste any on names. Everyone seems to be called things like Jop and Ko and Plop and Po. Jap and Ka and Mip and Fla. I wouldn't have minded a son called Erasmus or Rembrandt, but he'd have ended up as Ra or Bra. I did want my child to have a name, dammit, not just a cough or a fart.

'Ij have some very nice names!' he cried. 'Ij think these are perfekt. They are Dutch as well as English.'

'What are they?'

'Cecil, Doris and Agatha.'

Apparently, Cecil, Doris and Agatha are terrific names in Holland. Bang up to date. I had to explain that to call a defenceless baby Cecil in England would be a form of refined cruelty.

'He would start out in life with a terrible handicap.'

'He?' exclaimed Van Dyke. 'In Holland Cecil is a girl's name!' You see what we were up against.

In the end the name I fell for was Martha. Dark, mysterious, strong, isn't it? For a long time I kept this name a deep secret in my heart. Then, on a flying visit to my parents, some evil spirit tempted me to let loose my idea.'

'I quite like Martha,' I ventured.

'Not Martha!' shrieked my mother. 'I knew a woman called Martha when I was a girl – and she cut her throat!' Cutting someone else's throat wouldn't have been so bad and wouldn't necessarily mean the sacrifice of all pretensions to style. But cutting your *own*! So much for Martha. And so much for the name game. From now on my potential child was known to me, at least, as Old Baby. Perhaps Gloucestershire would supply the answer. And it might do so unexpectedly soon. For behold! The house purchase was completed!

I woke up to find myself scrubbing the floor. The Welsh floor. Scrubbing it goodbye. My energy had returned, miraculously, at the very moment when I needed it. By now it was the end of July. Good heavens! Where had the summer gone? I packed the pregnancy books. One fell open at a page which said 'Never move house when you are pregnant.' What was I supposed to do, then? Live in a cardboard box until I'd littered, like a stray cat? Goodness knows we had enough cardboard boxes. Van Dyke had been collecting them for weeks.

We packed all our possessions in them and still had enough cardboard boxes left to make an extremely important piece of modern sculpture. Instead we just left them in the yard, amongst all the bits of builders' debris. Dear debris! Who would take care of it when we were gone? Should we perhaps box it up and whisk it off to a new life in Gloucestershire?

One of the boxes had contained light bulbs. Van Dyke looked closely at the brand-name on the side.

'Mazda!' he cried.

'What?'

'Mazda! For a girl!'

'Eureka!' I whooped.

'Mazda Eureka Van Dyke!'

But we thought the better of it in the morning.

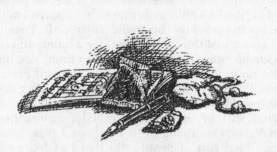

Chapter 9

I cried all the way to Gloucestershire. Darling old
Wales! How beautiful it was looking as we fled it!
Reproachfully splendid, with hawks hanging in its
sapphire skies, its oakwoods, rocks and waterfalls
more remote and wild than ever. The ancient glitter
of the Gower coast! The far-off roar of the Atlantic!
And its totally unpretentious people, of whom I had
been so afraid, and from whom I so oft had hid!
Lovely soft voices! Socialists to a man! Cunning,
subversive lot! So damned cuddly!

Our sweet little house! How faithful and warm it
had been! Its central heating had never failed us! Its
roof had not blown off! The poor dear cardboard
boxes we hadn't been able to use! How empty and
forlorn they looked out in the yard! Finished with!
Left to blow about in the lonely wind! Would the
bullocks miss us? Would the wild iris bloom unseen?

Waaaaah!

'Ij think it ijs your hormones,' remarked Van Dyke.
'Making you cry like this. It is said in the books you
might get weepje.'

Yes, I was crying cats and dogs. The tears were
streaming down my face so fast I was surprised I

wasn't getting thirsty. And since I was in the mood, I thought I might as well have a cry about everything else while I was at it. What always makes me cry most of all are the faint signs, here and there, of people trying to live like civilized human beings. An ambulance storms past and the traffic stops for it. Yes, the traffic *stops*. Just think about that for a moment! Why can't life be more like that more of the time? Boo hoo! On the radio we hear a BBC Teach Yourself French Course. People trying to learn each other's language! How sweet! Waaaah!

'What sort of people live in Gloucestershjire?' asked Van Dyke, tiring of this deluge. I was dumbstruck. What sort of people *did* live in Gloucestershire? True, I had grown up there, but children don't have quite the sociological perspective that Van Dyke was after. As we drove into the first low green bumps of the Cotswolds, I looked around. A lot of very distinguished houses of great antiquity were scattered discreetly among the trees (and none of those Forestry Commission blocks of melancholy pines, thank you very much. Oak and beech and birch and ash – trees that *do things*).

'Rich people,' I conjectured. In fact, I suddenly remembered with a surge of panic who did live around here. Royal People! Crumbs! The hills must be alive with plain-clothes detectives. Yes! Hadn't a mysterious figure in a trench coat just darted behind that oak tree?

They all had country retreats in Gloucestershire: the Prince of Wales just down the road; Princess Anne just up the hill; Prince Michael of Kent a stone's throw – I mean, I wouldn't dream – how shall I put it? – a carelessly tossed bouquet away. Why do they all live so close together? Is it so that, in the event of nuclear war, they can all be whisked away to safety in one of the Royal helicopters that ceaselessly beat their way across Gloucestershire skies? Or have they got a Royal nuclear bunker, tunnelled deep into the Cotswold limestone; a nice cosy underground palace called Bunkeringham Palace or Dunrulin'? I was beginning to have a few doubts about Gloucestershire.

The advantage of moving close to my parents was that we could stay with them and do all the moving bit gradually. The other advantage, of course, was that my parents could take care of us in our old age. Which, what with this moving business, was likely to be soon.

My mother welcomed us with an epic tea: salmon sandwiches, coconut cake, toasted teacakes and trifle formed a series of mighty peaks across the table, blotting out the sight of people on the other side. *Trifle*, by the way, is an extremely inappropriate name for my mother's version of this disgraceful pudding, of which jelly and custard form the deadly medium within which bananas, sponge-cakes, killer whales and Russian submarines have been deftly immobilized. Trifle, indeed! But then, the British always were ones for understatement.

'This is what is known as a British High Tea,' I explained to Van Dyke, the top of whose head was just visible above the salmon sandwiches.

'Ja – I understand,' he faltered. 'Ijt is *extremely* high.'

'Tuck in, Jonathan!' encouraged my mother (she is always about four boyfriends behind when it comes to names). 'You're going to need all your strength for this moving business.'

She was right. Next day No. 21 would become legally ours, and the vendor, Winnie Windbreaker, would move out. As we walked up the path to say hello, the tunnel of evergreens gave me a mild pang of foreboding. The house was so very sinister. Was it really our sort of house? Or a terrible mistake? And what were the people like round here? Was I going to go through the Welsh Cold Feet number all over again? Would Gloucestershire also turn out to be not home really, but a treacherous illusion? Would the siren song of London, albeit quieter now, never really fade from my jangling ears?

The front door was open. 'Hello!' we called into the dark void. 'Is there anybody there?' Was this a house purchase, I wondered, or a séance?

'Come in!' trilled a cheery voice from the Beyond. 'We've stopped for a tea-break!'

It was Winnie Windbreaker. We groped our way through to the kitchen where we dimly sensed a Presence. It was so dark in there, and so many guys with beards were sitting about, that at first I thought we'd blundered into a fresco of the Last Supper – before cleaning. All this darkness and coolness was very welcome, of course. You could have fried an egg on the pavement outside – if you hadn't been on a Spinach Only diet.

Winnie Windbreaker was a potter. On the dresser behind some of the disciples were a few of her plates. My word! What plates! They were enormous, and decorated with bold tides and swirls of Atlantic blue, forest green and gleams of gold. One didn't so much want to eat off them as spend the weekend in one. She had somehow managed to bring up four children in this house without losing her nerve, her energy or her looks. Well, when I say she hadn't lost her nerve, she wasn't terribly happy about gas.

'There's no gas!' she cried. 'Or at least there is gas but I've never used it! I'm always terrified it's going to blow up! And really this is very stupid, because my last house burned down because of an electrical fault!'

Van Dyke smiled quietly, but I sympathized deeply.

It's all very well for the Dutch. They're so damned pragmatic. I bet there isn't a Dutchman in the world who's frightened of gas or electricity. Me, I'm frightened of the most primitive technology. I'm frightened of the wheel. I know it's all the rage these days, but isn't it terribly *dangerous*? I was with Winnie Windbreaker all the way when it came to gas. I also liked the way she'd let the ivy grow up the walls, in through the windows and across the carpet. She was obviously deeply in tune with No. 21, and I felt very guilty for having dispossessed her.

She introduced us to her friends. The most overgrown turned out to be the local organizer of the Ecology Party. His name was Joe Oregano and he was a bit like John the Baptist, only with an eye for the ladies. *Doing anything tonight? Fancy a splash? Then maybe we could go on to the Kingdom of Heaven afterwards?*

'What do you do, Joe?' I asked.

'I teach macrobiotic gardening to mentally-handicapped adults,' he twinkled.

All I could think was how very much more worthwhile Oregano's work was than anything I'd ever done in my life. I'd felt pretty pleased with myself back there in Wales heaving those damned tadpoles about, but dear me! That was an esoteric self-indulgence compared to Joe's line of work. I was not able to admire him for long, however. He cycled off to organize something green.

Winnie's disciples finished their tea and flexed their sandals. It was time to be moving. Winnie's new home was only 300 yards up the hill. I felt extremely glad she would not be too far away. I knew we'd need her help and advice if her old house started to misbehave. And there was something exhilarating about her presence. Something windswept. I later discovered she was a Quaker, and I wasn't surprised. As we left them, the disciples carried out the plates, the giant flowerpots and the cat and wafted them uphill on a pillar of flame.

Or it might have been an old van. I didn't dare to look.

Next day we arrived to find the house very empty, very clean and rather shocked-looking. It had been inhabited by Winnie for over twenty years so the parting must have been a wrench. She had left us a welcome note, a list of useful phone numbers and a large and delicious cake. We immediately set about the exhausting business of having a cup of tea and eating the cake. Then, finally, irrevocably, the moment came when we had to move all our stuff in and start wreaking havoc in what had been a perfectly good house.

We did it all the wrong way round. First we moved all our boxes in and unpacked everything all over the floor, then we started repainting the ceilings. Soon everything was covered with white paint – except the ceilings. Some chemical reaction between our paint and the original varicose blue resulted in our white paint flaking off in huge blisters. Then we decided it might be a good idea to put down a few dust sheets. It wasn't all that long since we'd moved before but we seemed to have lost the knack of it.

A few days later, when we were up to the eyebrows in insulation (it was the hottest day of the year), Winnie Windbreaker breezed in carrying a wickerwork cradle.

'I thought you might like this!' she cried. 'I had a February baby, too, just after I'd moved into this house! A friend of mine made this for me so it's twenty-one years old! All my friends have borrowed it for their babies! You can rock it with your foot while you do the ironing!'

We put down our insulation (O, Fibreglass, where is Thy Sting? All down the left thigh and between the shoulder blades) and we gazed at the cradle. It was a close-woven, honeycomb-like little cell of willow, like something out of a medieval painting. I wished I was small enough to cuddle away in it myself.

90

Meanwhile Winnie was staring at her erstwhile donkey-brown walls.

'You're painting the walls a lovely white!' she cried. 'So am I, up at my house! Why did we all paint our houses these terrible dark colours? We must have been mad!'

Yes, we were turning our hand to the great whitewash. Or at least, I was. Van Dyke was doing the more manly stuff: hacking off plaster, heaving up floorboards, etc. We were helped, occasionally, by my two nephews who arrived from London in order to pull their muscles and get blisters in the interests of family unity. They were at the age when they didn't talk to grown-ups much, but they did a lot of secret sniggering, so they can't have been too fed up, I hope. They drew pictures on the walls of their least favourite people before hacking the plaster off with sharp instruments. This must be highly therapeutic.

Splashing white paint everywhere is also quite a turn-on. Not *too* white, you understand. I had fallen for the range of new, soft off-whites. The ad-man's dream. In the hall we had January (white with a hint of winter); in the sitting-room it was Blossom (white with a hint of spring); and in the bathroom it was Seagull (summery, seasidey, and dangerous to look up).

I could hardly believe how strong I felt these days. I painted room after room, from straight after breakfast to until 10 p.m. with only the briefest pauses for spinach and raspberry leaf tea. The baby did not get in the way at all, being at this stage no bigger than a mushroom. I was in that happy stage halfway through, when you feel on top of the world – or, in my case, on top of a stepladder.

More neighbours introduced themselves. On one side lived Sidney Arbour from Down Under, with her little girls Sam and Leone. Sidney, like Winnie, had separated from her husband and burst into luxuriant

91

life. Her girls were very beautiful. Sam had amber eyes which were going to cause a lot of people to walk into lamp-posts later. Leone was shy, haughty, and had more than a touch of Garbo about her. The life these girls lived with their unpredictable mama seemed, to the mere observer, dizzy but delicious. 'What shall we do this weekend, girls?' asked Sidney. 'Go camping in Wales? Go swimming and have a picnic? Or shall we sell the house?'

Sidney, it appeared, ran a travelling theatre group. I must admit that her tropical-print trousers and suspension-bridge earrings had aroused my suspicions. At last I was not ashamed to reveal the torrid truth: Van Dyke was a composer and I was a – well, sort of, *writer*. (Why does it always sound like a dirty word?)

Why are people of my age and generation so guilty about everything? We were the Peace Generation: born just after the war. Maybe that's why we can't stop turning the other cheek. I must admit I've often felt that two cheeks wasn't nearly enough.

'So you have trouble expressing your anger?' asks the expert.

'Do I? Gosh, I'm terribly sorry – maybe I do.'

Sorry, sorry, sorry. Sorry we were so well-fed and expensively educated. Sorry the jobs fell into our laps and the Pill into our mouths. Sorry we're so middle class. Sorry we went to university and then spent our time sitting in and dropping out.

Once we'd tried our hands at social experiment, radical politics, working-class vowels and Third World clothes we made our apologies and slipped into something more comfortable. The BBC, for example. Or writing. In a world where many have no work at all, some only back-breaking toil, and others mind-numbing routine, to admit you are a writer sounds outrageously cushy, somehow. Especially a comic writer. In the face of famine, unemployment and hard-line Socialist struggle, dare frivolity show her face?

To Sidney Arbour and Winnie Windbreaker, however, I dared to reveal the awful truth about what Van Dyke and I did for a living. I knew I could trust them to be interested, but not *too* interested. When you say you're a writer, or a composer, sometimes people go pale and excited and urge their chicken-poxed children to touch the hem of your raincoat. But Winnie and Sidney took it all in their stride. They were kind enough to read some of my writing. They wanted to hear some of Van Dyke's music. But they did not look at us as if we were from another planet.

It seemed Fate had steered our house-hunting footsteps towards an enclave of artists. Three doors down lived a painter and a photographer. Opposite them, a garden designer. Seven doors up, a silk screen printer. At my first antenatal class I met another painter, a girl from Mauritius whose husband was a sculptor. And they were all quite relentlessly delightful.

How very odd it was. The place was crawling with soul mates. All, no doubt, feeling terribly guilty. There's a constant, whistling sound that hangs in the air up here: the sound of thousands of lips murmuring sorry. So many of the self-employed gathered together! I bet the Tax Officer for the area is prematurely grey. I hope so, anyway.

Chapter 10

The advantage of being self-employed is that when you move house you can take two months off work for the plastering and painting. This is also the disadvantage of being self-employed. But there were some jobs at which even Van Dyke recoiled. Most of them were faults in the house's fabric which had been spotted by the Building Society's surveyor, whom Jove blast with boils. The faults included a disintegrating roof, rampant woodworm, and a tendency on the part of the back ground-floor room to sink for ever beneath the earth's crust.

On top of these essential jobs were the silly frivolous things we craved, such as a gas supply, central heating and bidets. Well, one bidet, anyway. I always used to consider bidets the most unnecessary of French affectations, but now, fundamentally wiser, I have come to regard them as the single device separating the barbarian from the Athenian. These days, thanks to my bidet, I am an Athenian from the waist down. It is some compensation for the increasing conviction that I am a barbarian from the neck up.

I had the bidet. But it was not connected. I ran next door to Sidney Arbour.

'I need a plumber!' I cried.

'Bill White,' pronounced Sidney. 'He's wonderful. He's sort of *joli laid*. And he's not expensive.'

I rang Bill White. He had a big gruff *joli laid* voice and a Cockney accent, and he promised to come round next day. Would he, I wondered, be *joli laid* like my favourite French film star, Gerard Depardieu? I could hardly wait. And next day when the doorbell rang, I beat Van Dyke to the door by a short head.

'Hello, Mr White!' I cried. Two small vole-like men in matching overalls stood there looking mystified.

'Er . . . we're from Servowarm,' the Vole Captain smiled. 'We've come to install the central heating.'

Servowarm had been doing a big promotion for their new customers that summer. *Win our competition*, they said, *and we'll pay off your mortgage*. Our mortgage was beginning to hang darkly over us like the Angel of Death, so we leapt at the chance. All you had to do apart from having central heating installed was to identify the historical period of four drawings of houses and Complete the Slogan.

The houses bit was easy. Idling an hour away in a bookshop, I stumbled upon the very book which Servowarm had used as source material. There the four drawings were, clearly identified! I bought it and raced home.

'Look!' I cried to Van Dyke. 'The Gods are on our side! Here are the Servowarm drawings! I told you that one was eighteenth century! All we need now is to Complete the Slogan.'

But what was the slogan? WITH MY MORTGAGE PAID OFF BY SERVOWARM I WOULD . . . What it needed was something short and snappy. Something memorable. Something they could use as advertising copy.

'I've got it!' I cried. 'With my mortgage paid off by Servowarm I would BE HOME AND DRY.'

Van Dyke looked doubtful. He could not, of course, appreciate the subtle word play involved, the association of warmth, safety and home with financial stability, a lifting of stress, and the gentle evocation of triumph. I still can't understand why it didn't win. But a few weeks later I was in a chemist's and I saw a pair of incontinence knickers called HOME AND DRY. Perhaps that had something to do with it.

I ushered the Servowarm voles in and they instantly began to make themselves burrows in the house, drilling runs through walls and lifting any floorboards not already lifted by Len. Ah yes, Len. We already had a Man At Work. Len was employed by a Damp and Decay Treatment company to kill the woodworm and fix the back room floor – the one that was sinking. Len was seriously fat and worked in nothing but a pair of white shorts. He was also prematurely bald and had huge jowls. All this conspired to give him the air of a gigantic but rather melancholy baby.

Fat Len had good reason to be melancholy. His company had taken on more work than they had men to do it, and Len was obliged not only to work alone but to have finished the job by last week. To this end he had spent the whole of Sunday, when any normal baby would've been cooing in the sunshine, getting to grips with the joists of our sitting-room: pulling out old rotten ones and putting in the new ones single-handed. I was reminded, as he juggled huge beams on his back, of the infant Hercules. I put my head round the door: it was time for his feed.

'Fancy a cup of tea, Len?'

'Ta!' Ta, you see. He even spoke Baby.

I rushed off to put the kettle on. But even as it began to sing, there was a ring at the front doorbell. That must be Bill White, the French film-star plumber, come to contemplate our bidet.

'Hello, Mr White!' Another pair of men in matching overalls stood there. There seemed to be a lot of them about this year.

'Gas Board,' said the small ferrety one, twitching his whiskers as if he was on the sniff for a gas leak right now. 'We've come to lay on a supply for you.' The other gasman appeared to be filled with it, blown up like a barrage balloon. He was enormous. Any minute now, surely, he would rise up above our pine trees and float off towards Oxfordshire. I wondered for a brief moment if he was to be installed at the corner of our house like a gasometer and pipes laid to link him up with our cooker.

'What we think we'll do, see,' said the ferrety one, 'is feed your new pipe up through the old pipe under the path.'

'Have we got an old pipe, then?'

'Ja,' said Van Dyke over my shoulder, 'but it is almost kompletely ruinated.'

Steam seemed to be pouring out of Van Dyke's ears. Was he coming to the boil? No, wait, it was the kettle that was coming to the boil. I dashed kitchenwards through the clouds of steam, marvelling at the wonders of modern gas technology. So they wouldn't even have to dig up the path! Just a hole in the road. How convenient. I just hoped that Mr Wolf's scaffolding wouldn't get in the way.

Ah yes, Mr Wolf. He'd been consulted about the disintegrating roof. He'd impressed us very much when he'd come to give the estimate. He was bald, cross-eyed, and desperately handsome.

'Do you want all the chimneys repointed, like?' he inquired, gazing skywards. I wondered for a moment just how many chimneys he could see. I hoped his estimate would not reflect his double vision.

As it turned out, the estimate was fine, so soon he and his silent mate came round and encased the house in scaffolding. Even now they were busying themselves about our bargeboards, somewhere up in the stratosphere. It is a very tall house. It made me dizzy looking up at them. When I brought them their tray of tea I used to place it on the ground and run inside. I couldn't face watching them climb down for it. Ten minutes later tea, cakes and biscuits were all gone, as if snapped up by some wild creature of the glens. But then, they were wild men, those two: refusing to come indoors, and slinking off to their muddy van to gnaw their lunchtime bones.

I made cups of tea for the Servowarm voles, for Fat Len the Damp and Decay baby, for the Gas Board ferret and barrage-balloon, and for the wolves on the roof. Van Dyke came into the kitchen.

'Can I hav a cup of tea?'

'No, you can't! We've run out of milk.'

'I'll hav it black, then.'

'We've run out of tea, too.'

'All right, I'll just have a cup of water, then.' But the tap hissed emptily. We had also run out of water. There was a knock on the door.

'Ah – now this really must be Mr White.' And it was.

'Good mornin', lovey,' he boomed from on high. I thought it was God for a minute, but the affectionate tone was all wrong. 'Bill White, plumber, at your service. Now let's have a look at this blessed bidet of yourn.'

Bill White had been a Sergeant-Major once, and retained all the dignity and authority of that office. He was seven feet tall, and had one of those old-fashioned British moustaches that bristle like a hawthorn hedge.

He surveyed the bidet and wash basin and seemed to think they presented no difficulty, but for reasons vaguely to do with gravity and drains, the bidet would have to be installed upon a kind of platform.

'Ij can build that for you,' offered Van Dyke.

'Right, guv'nor. Can you do it by Thursday?'

'Oh ja, certainly.'

'Right then. Thursday it is. We'll soon have you bouncing about on top o' that bidet like a ping-pong ball, lovey.'

Van Dyke set to work enthusiastically to build the platform. He had a gleam in his eye from which I had already learned to flee. Van Dyke loves manual work. It must be very soothing when your mind is jangling with flats and sharps and arpeggios. While he was banging away importantly I collected all the dirty teacups. I couldn't wash them though, because the water was still off.

'Come and look at my platform vor the bidet!' Van Dyke really has a flair for carpentry, I must say. The bidet-platform could have served as a stage for the Royal Shakespeare Company. I strode up and down on it ranting off a bit of *Hamlet*, but I couldn't help thinking: did it really have to be quite so *big*? Once one had scaled its heights it seemed like sacrilege to do anything less upon it than open Parliament.

It was never used, in the end. I think this was one of the saddest moments of Van Dyke's life. The bidet could not, after all, be installed where we'd originally intended.

'It's yer valves, you see, guv'nor,' explained Mr White. 'Suppose you're sitting there, lovey,' he always turned to me at moments of intense bidet-speculation, 'and somebody down in the kitchen turns on the cold-water tap, see ...' We couldn't understand the plumbing logistics of it, but it revolved around the concept of burnt bottoms. We let him install the bidet at the other end of the house, where the plumbing was plain sailing and no platform was necessary.

'Ah,' observed Mr White, glancing *en passant* at our newspaper, 'THE *Guardian*. A quid off the bill for that. I didn't see the bleeding *Daily Telegraph* round here the other day, did I?'

'No.'

'I should 'ope not.'

It was quite hard work keeping on the right side of Mr White politically speaking. It was quite hard work altogether having all these workmen around. Dammit, it was harder than doing the work yourself.

Try and take it easy, the pregnancy book had said. *Make sure you put your feet up and have a proper rest in the afternoons.* But put them up *where*? The sitting-room was full of up-ended floorboards. The landing was littered with Van Dyke's platform. Mr White was blasting away with his blow-torch on the first floor and the Servowarms were drilling their way towards oil in the kitchen. On the second floor Len was crashing about in search of woodworm, dressed in a night-marish mask and carrying a lethal spray. I lay down in our bedroom for a moment, but the window was filled with scaffolding and there was something unnerving about the way Mr Wolf's wolfish visage flashed to and fro there as he got to grips with our gable. It seemed rude to draw the curtains, so I got up instead.

I sought sanctuary in the front garden just as the gasmen got their pneumatic drill going outside our gate. They would, they informed me, have to dig up our path after all. I shrugged philosophically. At least if they dug up the path, no more workmen would be able to get to the house.

Winnie Windbreaker came scurrying down the street, and waved. I felt profoundly guilty. Her poor old house was being torn apart to the seams, and for no very good reason as far as I could see. I was spared the necessity of apologizing, though. Due to the pneumatic drill, we could not hear ourselves speak. With another wave she was gone – and for two pins I'd have gone with her. To the ends of the earth, preferably.

Eventually, though, peace descended. Len nailed down the last floorboard and packed his bags.

'Will the floor be strong enough to taak my grand piano?'

'He'll take seven grand pianos,' boasted Len, and jumped up and down, paunch and jowls flapping, to illustrate his faith in the structure. The Servowarm voles departed, leaving us with so many miles of piping it was clearly going to bankrupt us. The boiler always moaned while it was heating up: a long-drawn-out lugubrious wail like a dinosaur going into labour. And thanks to Mr Wolf's attentions, our roof was now rather more impenetrable than it had been. The bargeboards were all crisp and white and new. And as for the bidet – well, it reminded me of nothing so much as the fountains at Versailles.

It was all so stunning I had to invite my friend Alice down to inspect it. Alice is very small, and is very high up in the Civil Service. In fact, she's so small and so high up she's rather like the fairy on top of the Christmas tree. On the first morning of her visit I was washing up and humming to myself in time with the doleful wail of the boiler (and never was piping so sad), when suddenly out in the hall there was a great thump and a strange torrential sound. I glanced through the door and horrors! – water was spurting violently from the wall and cascading all over the flagstones.

'Help! Flood!' I cried, grabbing a broom and opening the front door.

The cry of *Flood* must have stirred something deep and atavistic in Van Dyke's nature, for he leapt to the rescue and immediately started to build a dyke to keep the water from the sitting-room. Meanwhile I swept the water out of the front door, on and on like the Sorcerer's Apprentice from *Fantasia*.

'Where's your stopcock?' inquired Alice at my ear.

'I don't know!' I cried. 'Shall I call the Fire Brigade?'

'There must be one out in the road,' mused Alice, and then slipped through the spray and disappeared down the front path.

'You sweep!' I cried to Van Dyke, who had completed his sea-wall.

'What are you calling me? It is not my fault!'

'No: you sweep, it's a verb, not an insult! You sweep, and I'll call the Fire Brigade!' I pressed the broom into Van Dyke's hand.

It was my first ever emergency call. 999. Boy, was I excited. It took so long for the dial to spin round. We could've drowned, waiting for the damn nines to register. Why don't Emergency Services have the number 111 instead? Or even just 1?

'What service do you require?' asked a bored voice.

'Water is spurting all over my hall!' I cried.

'Which service do you require?' she repeated. Some people seem to want to be mistaken for answering machines.

'I think I want the Fire Brigade. They deal with floods, don't they? Burst water mains and things?'

'Which service do you require?' No, she wasn't nearly as animated as an answering machine. I asked for the Fire Brigade anyway. But the minute I put the phone down, the jetting water stopped.

Alice came wandering back up the path. 'There's a stopcock in the street,' she explained. 'I turned it off.'

Alice was probably the only person I knew whose arms were slim enough to reach down the tiny aperture – down which, normally, the Water Board men insert a kind of enormously long thin spanner. Fancy even knowing it was there to be turned off! Alice's brilliance seemed to extend from the heights of the Civil Service to the bedrock of street-wisdom.

A solitary fireman in an ordinary saloon car soon

arrived, and I realized that, as emergencies went, ours wasn't. He said the leak was due to old lead piping and mended it there and then for us. I would have made him a cup of tea if the water hadn't been turned off.

Later, Alice noticed a much more evil trickle of water escaping from a manhole cover on our path. She pointed it out to me.

'What's that?' I trembled.

'It looks like blocked drains,' she murmured. Jack next door happened to be going down his path at the time, and I inquired whether he had a set of rods we could borrow. Within thirty seconds he was in his boiler suit and round at our house, had the manhole cover off and was rodding away for dear life. I took one peep into the manhole and ran.

Jack rodded on, though. The sun set, and the stars came out, and Jack rodded on. At one point he decided he needed a different attachment, and drove off to Cirencester to get it – a round trip of eighteen miles. He couldn't be stopped. He had a galloping case of good neighbourliness. The moon rose, the vixen howled on the hill, and Jack was still rodding away by torchlight. His wife Jill stood by her back door to assist with witty observation. 'Van Dyke should write a piece of music to celebrate this,' she suggested. 'A piece for pipe band. Starting with a long slow movement.'

In the end Jack had to admit he was beat. He had, he said, got his rods down as far as the front gate. It seemed to me he'd got them down as far as the South of France. But down beyond the front gate was a mysterious obstruction.

Next day the council workmen came and dug a hole, which filled up with foul water, and it appeared that the gasmen had, in the course of giving us a gas supply, broken our main sewage pipe. I expect the huge barrage-balloon man had trodden on it.

Eventually they came to put it right, but for a while we were cut off from the world by a moat in which the germs of 127 infections could be seen to be breeding. Jill finally got them to come and fill the hole in by a series of enraged phone calls at hourly intervals. She was obviously much more adept than we were at being a householder and enraged ratepayer.

I was beginning to have an inkling of what it meant, being a householder. We seemed to be holding ours together with our bare hands much of the time. The bits of it not collapsing or exploding as part of the natural course of things were being deftly undermined by the great British Workman.

Putting my feet up on Van Dyke's platform for a rare moment of prenatal rest, I gazed enviously at my belly. Lucky Old Baby! It knew nothing of our trials. I was consumed with a longing to crawl back into the womb myself. But I'm not sure that my mother would've been all that co-operative.

Chapter 11

Eventually we stopped working on the house. It wasn't so much that it was finished. It was more a case of our realizing it never would be finished. Six or eight weeks previously we had argued furiously about colour schemes.

'We *must* have contrasting white gloss on the woodwork!' I screeched. 'Or it'll look *silly*! And get on my *nerves*!'

'Ijt is absolutely not my opinion,' insisted Van Dyke. 'Ijt will make the room look smaller.'

'But the room's enormous anyway! What does it matter if it looks a bit smaller? And it won't be much of a contrast anyway, for God's sake. The walls will be white too – only a different shade of white.' (Ivory White, actually – white with a hint of dead elephant.)

Yes, two months ago we had really cared about shades of white! Now the wretched woodwork lay unpainted in any shade of white at all: in parts it was still naked wood. And did it get on our nerves? We didn't even notice. Naked wood was nothing. There was a vast rubble-filled hole in our kitchen wall where the Rayburn had been torn out (I did warn you

I was a barbarian from the neck up). And we co-existed happily with the rubble-filled hole for almost two years.

In short, the nesting instinct began to pall, thank God. It gave way to much more interesting preoccupations such as curiosity to discover where on earth we were. In terms of crude geography, if you leaned out of your top window and looked down to your right, beyond the town, you could see the sun setting over the Severn plain with its great airy space, blue and far. If you looked up to your left you'd see wooded hills leading up to the great Cotswold plateau, stretching away and away as far as Oxford. Stroud grew up where five deep river valleys meet, not far from the escarpment where the limestone plateau, scored with rushing streams, collapses into the broad water-meadows of the big river.

That's what it said in the books, anyway. Yes. I'd got as far as the local library, and had plundered as many books on Gloucestershire as I could balance on my belly. It was much more fun reading about the five deep river valleys than the three sorts of prenatal stress syndrome. My excursions into local history were particularly fascinating. History's great. You know it's never going to rear up and bite you, which is more than you can say for the future. And what's more, it's our destiny. We're all irrevocably becoming history. I am, anyway. Especially round the neck.

'Hey!' I cried to Van Dyke. 'Palaeolithic man hunted mammoth and rhino in Gloucestershire!'

'Who?' murmured Van Dyke from the depths of a book. He was catching up with his reading, too (*Existentiële Fenomenologie*). I tried to explain to him the difference between the Palaeolithic guys with their macho Stone Age nonsense ('Me Tarzan, you Mammoth, take that you bastard!') and those frightfully nice Neolithic people who turned up in 2000 BC and started keeping herds and making pottery and growing plants. They were the founders of the Green Movement, really, but it wasn't very big in those days because the main problem facing the average householder was not the decline of the forests but how to keep them out of his bedroom.

I could see Van Dyke was dying to get back to his Existential debate ('Objectiviteit en objectivisme . . .') so I plunged alone into the Bronze Age, and was delighted to discover there the systematic cultivation of cereals – in other words, the dawn of muesli. It was the dawn of medals, too. Bronze ones – or third place. The ones we British occasionally manage to win. We're so aquiescent as a nation – apart from the odd bulldog – that I was not surprised to learn that back in the pre-Christian era our local Gloucestershire tribe was regularly beaten up by the wild Welsh Silurians, especially on Saturday nights.

'Our local tribe was the Duboni,' I remarked. 'Do you think that's pronounced *Dubonnet?*' But Van Dyke was lost in *De Immanentie van de kennis.*

The Duboni were a bit effete and artistic. We imported fine metal work, Italian pottery and other luxuries. Yes, we Duboni really had what you might call a life style. But when not being harassed from the west by the Silurians, we had to contend with raids from the south. It was a case of, 'Oh my gods, here come the Belgi.'

The Belgi invaded Britain in the first century BC and started minting coins. To my mind, things have gone steadily downhill ever since. We Duboni were managing perfectly well with our iron bars, thank you very much. OK, they were over half a metre long and they made your handbag clank a bit, but if anyone tried to mug you, you could always whip one out and hit him over the head with it. Try doing that with one of our modern pound coins.

Still, what can you do with guys who invent money? We married them, of course, and became known as the Belgi-Duboni. The Roman Emperor Claudius, however, was soon going to put all our little local squabbles into perspective: in AD 43 he dispatched an army of invasion, and that was that. Or nearly.

There was a local chieftain, Caractacus, and there is a theory that he holed up on what is now Minchinhampton Common, a plateau just south of Stroud, after being defeated by the invading Romans under Plautius. The plateau is dotted with extensive earthworks, and walking up there one day for a bit of fresh air I could almost see old Caractacus and his cronies prowling round their camp, with the wind and the thistles and the woad.

'Hey! Van Dyke!' I cried. 'I think this is where Caractacus hung out!'

'I think you have spent enough money on plants already this week.'

I wondered whether to persevere, to try and make my obsession with local history part of my marriage, but the exotic attractions of Caractacus were too urgent for laborious explanation. Even now I saw a Roman legion clinking along the valley floor on their way from Aquae Sulis and wily old Caractacus pushing boulders over into them from his hiding place in the beechwoods.

Caractacus (played by Donald Sutherland in a red beard – his eyes, I reckon, are perfect Belgi) emerged four years later as the leader of the Silures in Wales. Evidently they had patched up their differences in an attempt to kick the Romans out. The usual gallant but futile British gesture. When in AD 47 Ostorius Scapula (played by Sylvester Stallone) succeeded Plautius (played by Marlon Brando) the Roman army were kept quite busy with guerrilla raids by Caractacus and his buddies. Tacitus (played by Al Pacino) wrote the original script, but my agent will handle film rights inquiries on his behalf.

The Romans won in the end, of course. And frankly, most of us Belgi-Duboni must have had a sneaking sense of relief when they finally got us in an arm-lock and started imposing civilization on us. It must've been like Christmas. Although it was a bit early for that – Christ himself had only been dead about ten years.

Just think what the Romans had to offer: central heating, roads ('Roads?' sneered the old Duboni sages. 'They'll never catch on.') And then all those endless baths. Chedworth Roman villa, north-east of Stroud, has two substantial sets of baths, just for one household. No queuing for the bathroom in those days. And baths were communal anyway. Much more fun. I don't think the disastrous influence of Christianity upon bathing habits has been fully explored.

I'd always associated this part of Gloucestershire with the Romans. My parents had been living in North Woodchester, two miles from Stroud, since 1970. Of the fifty or so Roman villas known to have existed in the Cotswolds, the most splendid was at Woodchester. I took Van Dyke there. None of the Roman villa is visible today. It lies buried beneath the old churchyard. The Norman church is now just a ruin: an archway and a couple of fragments of masonry.

There's a melancholy avenue of yews, and I led Van Dyke deep into the wet grass one evening, trying to explain that beneath the crumbling twelfth-century stonework, beneath the grass, beneath the earth, lay a sight infinitely more ancient, and much more alive.

'There's a great big pavement under here,' I explained. 'It's about fifty feet square – what's that in metres – er, divide by three, and add ... well, it's huge. It's a mosaic of the Orpheus legend.'

'A Norman pavement?'

'No, no – a Rorman – I mean *Roman* pavement.'

'Built by Caractacus?' He was trying hard – but imagine trying to get to grips with Dutch history of the second century.

'No – Caractacus was a Briton. The pavement was part of a big Roman palace. I mean, an administrative centre. There were sixty-five rooms.'

The Orpheus pavement is exposed to view every few years, but there is not enough money to roof it over and pay a custodian, so after a few weeks of summer sun on its face, and the curious eyes of thousands of visitors delighted by its beauty, it is carefully covered again. And so they all go into the dark: the lively leopard, the bear, the stag, the lithe lioness and tigress; the peacocks, dove and hen, the pheasant and the fox, and Orpheus himself. There's the hum of music under the earth at Woodchester.

It's a curious place. As a pregnant woman I felt at home there. Hidden life, buried deep. I couldn't really expect Van Dyke to understand, as a man and as a Dutchman. Dig a hole in England and you find Roman mosaics. Dig a hole in Holland and you'll drown. I know the English and the Dutch are very alike, but sometimes we both feel it's a very *mixed* marriage.

And speaking of mixed marriages, how did it work out with the Roman invaders and the conquered British tribes? Was there, one wonders, respect, affection, maybe a little hanky-panky? How many of today's young Gloucestershire girls with their weird teased hairstyles and eyelids black with make-up carry Roman blood in their veins? There must have been a fair amount of intermingling before the Romans upped and ran, like people who suddenly realize they've left the gas on at home. They ran right into the explosion, and that was the end of Rome not just in Britain but everywhere else as well. A different sort of Roman is garrisoned in Gloucestershire

110

now, at the US Air Force bases, and their jets regularly cut the air in half as if they were lords of the world. Ha! Their turn will come.

But right after the Romans, it was the Saxons' turn, and then, in the eleventh century, the Normans'. I've never been wholeheartedly in favour of the Norman invasion, although I know it was a good thing, administratively and commercially. They seem a colourless mob, with their bureaucracy and efficiency, after the dashing, flashing Saxons. And the Saxons had much better words. *Wolf*, for example. Now that's a real word. No messing about. The Saxons had the best rude words, too.

Still, I have to admit that the Nomans founded a tradition of building in Gloucestershire in which the peculiar beauties of our local limestone spring to life in shapes which complement the steep hills and the dark masses of hanging woodland. The limestone is called oolite, which means 'eggstone', and it is an almost luminous honey colour, glowing in the shade, gleaming in the sun, and fading gently to a warm grey under centuries of mild rain.

'I must find out about limestone!' I cried, rushing through centuries of mild rain to the library. Van Dyke looked apprehensive. Was this my first Strange Longing? We'd heard of pregnant women eating coal, but limestone? It gave new meaning to the idea of a cottage cheese diet. But it would certainly build strong bones and teeth. In fact, the odd limestone sandwich would probably be a jolly good thing, as long as the baby didn't turn out to be an azalea.

In the library I discovered that the woman who knew all about the Cotswolds was Edith Brill. *Old Cotswold, Cotswold Crafts, Tropic of Cotswold* – you name it. I borrowed them all and dived straight in, reading the first one on the way home, so great was my longing for limestone – the True Story.

Edith Brill delivered the goods. Immediately I was

111

initiated into the vocabulary of the Cotswold slater (the guy who makes the stone roof-tiles and covers the buildings with them). 'The slates used under the eaves were called Cussomes or Top-eaves, those next in size being known as Followers. A slat-rule illustrated in Margaret Westerling's *Country Contentment* gives twenty-six names for different sizes ... Long Pricks, Long Cuttings, Short Becks, Middle Becks, Short Wivetts and Long Wivetts, and two with the intriguing names of Long and Short Bachelor. Duchesses and Countesses are still familiar today, and I was once given Movedays and Cocks by a shy young slater. (But the seventeenth-century writer Randall Holme's Rogue-why-Winkest-thou, Jenny-why-gettest-thou, his Farwells, Chilts and Warnetts seem to have vanished from the slate-makers vocabulary, and it is difficult to imagine anyone using them nowadays without the fear of being thought long-winded and pretentiously olde-worlde.)'

A few days later, Van Dyke and I lingered in Bisley – our nearest village, famous as the abode of the blonde bombshell bestselling lady novelist. Since I am more dark and remaindered than blonde and bestselling, my eyes were fixed firmly on the roof-tiles. But Van Dyke was keen for a glimpse of the great lady.

'Where does Diana Cooper live, exactly?'

'Jilly.'

'Where's that?'

'Is that a Long Prick up there, I wonder? Or is it a Moveday or a Cock? I wish I could tell the difference.'

'Is that her, over there?'

'Cussomes!'

'Bless you!'

My attempts to introduce Van Dyke to the intricacies of Cotswold crafts were as fruitless as his own attempts to cast admiring glances at Ms Cooper. She remained obstinately hidden beneath what I am sure are some very distinguished Rogue-why-Winkest-thous (an appropriate slate, I think you'll agree, for the lady in question).

'Back to the library!' I cried. 'I must get into wool!' Van Dyke approved of this. He never did like that Polypropylene. And it hasn't got the history, either. Round here, wool is history. And history is wool.

Much of Gloucestershire's wealth, which produced the proud churches and the beautiful manor houses with their quaintly-named slate roofs, came in the usual hard-nosed way. The business was wool. Even before the Romans wool production had thrived. There were upland pastures suitable for sheep; there were racing streams in the valleys for the washing, fulling and dying of the finished cloth.

'Hey!' I cried. 'Listen to this! Do you know how they finished the cloth? They hammered it in troughs of clear running water until the wool fibres felted together. Imagine thinking of doing that! How completely weird!'

'And listen to this,' rejoined Van Dyke, also reading, 'Het ware *cogito* is niet la tête-à-tête de la pensée avec la pensée de la pensée.' A hive of intellectual activity, our house. His bit, anyway.

'Capitalism thrived in the Stroud valleys!'

'The bastaards!'

'Yes. You see, the valleys round here filled up with mills, and the gentlemen clothiers who owned them got richer and richer while the weavers who did the work could barely manage to survive.'

Stroud is full of weavers' cottages, with their large upper windows to let in as much light as possible on to the looms. Once I began to read and think about the place I suddenly began to see it. And I realized at last why Stroud is so different from the rest of the Cotswolds: why it falls short of the immaculate and exquisite beauty of Painswick, which used to be a wool town, too. The reason was simple. Steam.

Steam came to the trade in the nineteenth century, but Stroud alone rose to the industrial challenge and continued to expand. In all the other Cotswold wool towns the trade and the population began to decline. The north of England had seized the commercial initiative, and as Edith Brill puts it, in *Portrait of the Cotswolds*, 'except for Stroud, which partially adopted the use of steam as well as water power after 1830, and which continued to grow into a factory town with the usual sprawl and litter of late-nineteenth-century industrialism, the region lost little of its Cotswold charm.'

Any visitor can see at once what Edith Brill means by sprawl and litter. Stroud's valleys are still full of mills and small factories. Beautiful old limestone mills and less beautiful brick ones. And the twentieth century's distinguished contributions to architecture – asbestos, concrete and corrugated iron – can be seen to glorious effect here and there. Old sheds, brick terraces of houses, Victorian builders' yards, and a disused canal contribute little to Cotswold charm.

So whereas the surrounding villages such as Painswick, Bisley and Minchinhampton are immaculate and austere in their unspoilt antiquity, Stroud has a more scruffy, compromised, busy air. It has an unfinished feel to it, with empty shops in the High Street, large-scale renovation works in progress, and plans for more changes in the future, hotly debated in the Council Chamber, the press and in the streets.

Because of this, house prices in Stroud are lower than in the surrounding villages, which is why Van Dyke and I could afford to go and live in Gloucestershire at all. But aside from financial consideration, I preferred the sprawl and litter of Stroud, the atmosphere of bustle and rebuilding, the mixture of red-brick terraces with limestone cottages. The mongrel

114

is always the most vital of dogs, and perhaps of towns too.

I wouldn't want to live in exquisite Painswick, though. Nor, I think, in any of the villages. I'd realized, halfway through house-hunting, that I wasn't ready for village life. To be frank, it scares me stiff. The silence, for a start – especially at night. Whenever I've slept in the country I've felt the huge black hairy silence force its way through my bed-room window and sit on my head until I can hear the blood booming in my ears. And so, probably, could everyone else in the village.

And it's impossible to have a private life in a village. Everybody knows everything. Imagine it! The possibility of St Peter writing it all down in The Book is bad enough, but the certainty of Miss Hopkins writing it all down in her diary is unbearable. '17th May. That Anglo-Dutch baby across the road is crying again. Still, what can you expect, with those parents? Even as I write I can smell burning toast. They've both been married before of course – that's a v.v. telling fact, I feel. Still, one must be charitable. I shall go over there in a moment and give them a pot of my quince jelly.'

And then there's crime. They say there isn't any in the country. Well, there isn't any for eight years and five months and six days. Then on the seventh day a maniac bursts into your kitchen with a sawn-off shotgun and that's it. Whereas in the small town, apart from the noise, the bustle, and the possibility of anonymity, there's the reassuring sound at night of a gang of teenagers going up the street ripping off all the car aerials. But, since it's a small country town, only the car aerials. What more could one hope for, these days? So it seemed to me that Stroud, with its industrial debris and far from immaculate backyards, sheds and warehouses, was the perfect place to be.

Mind you, despite all the allure of Stroud's sprawl

and litter, it was still two months before I let up on
the decorating enough to go out and explore the
place. But one morning, when the paint had run out
(Eyeball – white with a hint of hangover) I decided
to walk down into town and sniff around. Walking
down into a town is always a pleasant plunge,
reminding one of seaside towns of one's childhood,
and this one, ringed by its green, inhabited, almost
Tuscan hills, was beautifully situated.

Here was a lovingly rebuilt medieval hall: there, a
tiny old-fashioned sweetshop with bulging Dicken-
sian windows; here, a dingy hardware shop with a
range of splendid crowbars on the wall. There were
several unrepentantly nineteenth-century drapers,
with their curiously touching window displays of
knickers, warm pyjamas and tea towels. There was a
splendid bookshop, with a separate children's shop
and a huge secondhand department, run by Alan and
Joan Tucker. I remembered a time when this shop
had been run from a tiny kiosk-sized shop near the
station: I used to loiter in it when visiting my parents.
Now it had moved across the road into grander
premises, and one had the feeling that the Tuckers'
books were secretly invading room after room of
central Stroud.

Little lanes and alleyways darted here and there,
with old pubs leaning against the steep gradient: The
Pelican, The Swan, The Fleece. There was the
occasional characteristically Gloucestershire shop,
such as the saddler's, but for the most part Stroud
seemed wonderfully ordinary and unpretentious.
There were no highly polished antique shops: none,
at least, that I would have been intimidated to enter.
There was a market with fish and cheese stalls. And
there was no barging, no bumping, no ratty metro-
politan struggle. People in the shops had time to chat
and be genial. What was this? Ordinary life?

I was standing in the greengrocer's shop, revelling

116

in the Harvest Festival smell of it all; and the golden shine of the grapefruit and the deep blush of the first English apples, and the satisfying ranks of green things that grow above and beneath and upon the earth, waiting peacefully for my turn at the till and feeling quite pleased with life, when it happened. A small but determined foot kicked me – from the inside.

Chapter 12

Long before the baby started beating me up from within I had been talking to it in secret. Somehow it helped me to believe in its existence, even back in the early days when it was too small to be noticeable.

'You're about as big as a mushroom now,' I'd whispered in a public loo in Neath. 'It says so in the book, oh Scoobie Woobie Phoobie Doobie Doobie Doo.'

Sickening, isn't it? Nineteen years earlier, in the shadowy depths of a Cambridge college, I'd discussed the Platonism of Marsilio Ficino, and occasionally even uttered things like 'Benedictus Deus in donis Suis, et Sanctus in omnis operibus ...' And hark at me now.

'Ooolie Ooolie, OO, you incorrigible old Poo Rockabye baby in a Welsh loo.'

One woman in her time speaks many tongues.

Once the baby had begun to make its presence felt by its dancing and fossicking about and its relentless expansion, my attention turned towards it even more. I became absurdly preoccupied with the life within, to the exclusion of the life without. And the life without seemed more than ever twisted and frightening. I could hardly bear to watch News Programmes on TV. The wider world seemed night-marish: famines, fires, murders and riots; children choking to death in outbreaks of poison gas; wars and rumours of wars. Not to mention the nuclear war-heads waiting in their satanic hiding-places. I was ashamed at the world that was waiting for my baby.

Our immediate environment was more encourag-ing, though. Autumn came stealing over the land-scape and as I looked at the yellowing trees and the swept-clean ploughed fields and the clouds of birds wheeling away to the south, I liked the thought of my child's eyes seeing all this, next year. If indeed there was a next year. And if, indeed, there were eyes.

Suddenly the world was an infinitely dangerous place, full of thoughts that made you shake with a sense of the unbearable. A robin sang his autumn song.

'Do you hear that, Old Baby?' I inquired. I began to wonder how many sounds of the life outside reached it, through the drum of skin, the roar of waters and the thump of blood.

Sidney Arbour dropped in from next door, and startled me by telling us how her younger daughter Leone had been born ten weeks prematurely and had weighed only 2 lb. *Ten weeks!* Ours was due in early February. That meant that even as early as this ... I looked around in panic. Nothing was ready. Winnie Windbreaker's wickerwork cradle was waiting. But where was everything else? What would keep it warm? What would it wear? Look at? Play with?

But still I hesitated. I was suffering a form of mental torment common in pregnancy. Suppose you have several drawers full of little vests and jumpers and bootees, and then ... and then the unspeakable happens. The damned books were no help: every time I opened one, a list of horrifying complications leapt off the page. The dangers the mother faced were frightening enough. I'd already had Costal Margin Pain all down my Atlantic seaboard and was awaiting, with terror, Carpal Tunnel Syndrome, the Butterfly Mask and Personality Changes. They all sounded like a Hitchcock trilogy. But I was a realm of terror beyond mere Hitchcock.

What if something happened to the baby? Several times a day I had this thought and had to run away to a secret place so the tears could bounce off the walls without alarming anybody. Every time I opened a newspaper or magazine, or switched on the radio or TV, there was some poor woman talking about the death of her baby.

I remembered how, when I was a callow schoolgirl, a neighbour's baby had died and I had wondered if perhaps losing a baby wasn't quite as bad as losing a grown-up, because a baby hadn't, in some sense, really started to be somebody. Now I understood that it was ten times worse. And the thought of the empty vests, folded in their drawer and waiting for the warm body in vain, was so terrible that I hadn't got a single vest in the house.

I was rescued from these hesitations by my friend from the north. I'll call her Tyger, because she does tend to burn bright in the forests of the night. She rang me up on a windy night in December, on a particularly bad line.

'What do you XAXAPLXA?' she inquired.

'What do I what?'

'KAKAPLXSKAKA need?'

'What do I need? I need tranquillizers.'

'No, I mean you might be able to use a few XAXAXAK. And I've SZPLZDZ some old KAKA-KAKA bought in Keighley and run in the wash, they're pink, but KZAXZAXZAX. And then there's a SZAPLLDXA chair and a ZAKZAKZAK and a trav

120

XTPXTPXTP you might find useful. We'll bring them down.'

A week later Tyger arrived on our doorstep, accompanied by her husband (let's call him Lamb, as he is woolly and bright and at his best at Sunday lunchtime). They had left their child with his grandparents in order to make room in their car for everything I needed. I watched in astonishment as they unpacked a series of completely mysterious objects. That armful of metal tubes must be the SZAPLLDXA, and perhaps that square contraption with the nylon mesh was the ZAKZAKZAK.

'This,' began Tyger, unfolding the square thing with mesh, 'is a travel cot.' ZING! It sprang, at her expert touch, into a coherent and inviting shape, suggestive of golden slumbers.

'And this ... is the bouncing chair ...' Lamb dextrously screwed some tubes together to form a tiny reclining chair. But what was that sinister object with the hooks and the wheels? Was it, as it appeared to be, a bird of prey with four-wheel drive? Snap! Ker-splok! At Tyger's bidding it performed a cartwheel, and lo and behold! It was a pushchair. (The hooks were handles.)

'We didn't find that terribly useful,' observed Tyger, 'because of having no roads where we live, let alone pavements.' They live on the moors, within haunting distance of Wuthering Heights.

'But we used this nearly every day,' she went on, flourishing a denim octopus at us. It turned out to be a baby-carrier or sling. She strapped it on to Van Dyke and we coaxed the largest of my ancestral teddy bears into the baby's seat. That teddy bear had no idea what was in store for it. Its peaceful retirement would soon be shattered, its ancient ears mercilessly mauled and its dulled eyes poked. But for the moment these attentions were all devoted to my tenderest bits of womb-furniture.

121

Lamb went back out to the car, and Tyger explained that she hadn't brought us much in the way of clothes: just the things she'd found most useful. Then Lamb came in again bearing a large pile of what I guessed was KAKAKAKA, some of which bore signs of having run in the wash.

'This is a changing mat,' explained Tyger, flourishing a large spongy vinyl square. She didn't explain what it changed into, though. For one wild moment I wished it would change into a magic carpet and waft me off to Tel-El Kebir. The sheer volume and complexity of all the equipment made my head reel. How green I had been. And how lucky to have such friends from the north.

Other friends of ours who had also had children behaved with the same determined generosity. Van Dyke's sister, who lived in France, gave us a carrycot packed with French baby clothes, once, no doubt, chic, but now crackling with antiquity. There was also a pile of French nappies which looked mysteriously like table napkins. In fact – but I'd better not go into all that in case you ever come to dinner.

From France also my sister-in-law brought some lovely new baby suits, from Aix-en-Provence; of such exquisite, velvety, powder-blue softness that they made one's heart ache. They made my heart ache, anyway. But it took very little to make my heart ache, these days. If it wasn't the TV news being unbearably horrible, it was yet another parcel of clothes and toys from helpful friends. Either way, I cried.

Van Dyke wasn't quite so deeply involved in the emotional peaks and troughs, of course. After all, it was my hornomes that were getting the show on the road. And besides Van Dyke had had a baby before. He already had a seventeen-year-old daughter by a previous marriage: a graceful and glowing young lady of many talents and no visible vices. She lived with her mother in Holland, and visited now and then.

So I was a stepmother. Unfortunately, I'd been too busy being pregnant and moving house and trying to finish writing a novel before I finished the baby to give myself up to my traditional duties as stepmother. I hadn't even found time to lock her up in a tower with nothing but a bowl of gruel to eat and a bushel of wolf's hair to spin and weave into a magic jogging-suit by midnight. It's terrible feeling one has neglected one's family responsibilities. But just getting my own baby organized seemed to take for ever.

But while people who were already parents gathered supportively round, my childless friends seemed to grow small and distant, like people left behind on a station platform. I'd always belonged to their club, and celebrated their life of spontaneous theatre visits, weekends walking in the hills, and silent Sunday mornings unfolding over toast and newspapers at 10 a.m.

We'd exchanged meaningful glances whenever a dreadful child-tyrant had gone into one of its routines within fifty yards of us. We'd recoiled in distaste from the manic monologues of motherhood.

'So little Angela was on the breast for eighteen months!' I'd mimicked, escaping from one such domestic scenario, 'so who cares?' Actually, now, I was beginning, if not to care exactly, at least to be interested. Eighteen months? Really? Tell me more! Yes, I was becoming interested in babies! I could feel my allegiance changing. At this curious moment of my life, however, carrying about inside me a stranger who was palpably alive, and yet still not having consciously to care for it, I seemed to belong to a half-world poised between childlessness and parenthood. It seemed miraculous beyond belief that small hands, intricate ears and eyelashes had already taken shape within me. I gazed at mothers pushing prams and longed to stop and marvel at it all with them. They did not look ripe for an attack of

123

marvelling though. They just looked tired and ratty.

The only people who might share my state of mind were other women also expecting their first baby. And at last I was to meet a few. Realizing I had everything to learn I enlisted at the local Health Centre for a course of antenatal classes. Every Thursday afternoon I lumbered down the hill and joined four or five other pregnant women – at least two young enough to be my daughters. We were all expecting our first baby. The two I got to know best were Candide, a painter from Mauritius who radiated serenity, and Sheila, a computer programmer from up the hill who radiated panic. Every week, it seemed, Sheila's eyes grew more huge and harelike with dreadful speculation. 'What if . . . and what if . . .' She was uncontrollably imaginative, especially in the realm of dire emergency. Candide, however, seemed enviably relaxed. Every week she grew more sleek and smooth until she seemed to emit a kind of golden light, damn her. Maybe this was the Second Coming, or something.

'Have you thought of any names?' I asked her one day.

'We thought of calling it after a Dogon village.'

'A what?'

'An African village.'

Her husband had also been brought up in Africa, so I suppose it was natural and easy for them, when thinking of babies' names, to consider that of a Dogon village. For a split second I revolved, fairly feverishly, the possibility of calling our baby after a Gloucester-shire village. How about, say, Bourton-on-the-Water Van Dyke? It was appropriately aquatic. And the baby's Dutch cousins could call it – for short.

When it came to my own mental state, I alternated between sharing Sheila's panic and generating some even more acute panic of my own. However, I kept telling myself that it would be all right. Since I was so

124

old, I wouldn't get in such a state as I might have ten years previously, would I? And what's more, since all my friends had had their babies already we'd inherited all their equipment and could no doubt call upon them for advice. So that was a good thing, too.

And though the Older Mother may be a little short on energy, think of the experience of life in general one brings to the business at this great age. Ripeness is all, isn't it? I certainly didn't mind waddling about like a pumpkin, or missing the discos. I'd been to enough damned discos in my time to last until Domesday. In fact some of them had been not unlike Domesday themselves, complete with clientèle recently risen from the dead.

And as for losing my looks, well, they'd gone long ago. The natural bloom, that is. What a will o'the wisp thing one's bloom is! Girls in Jane Austen lose it and regain it overnight. My bloom had never had a chance. In my early teens it was defeated by hockey and scowling tomboyism; in my late teens by politics and scowling scholarship. Then there were my twenties: teaching in a comprehensive school and having three migraines a week doesn't do a lot for your bloom. My early thirties in London were more promising, but by then I was too thin.

I've got an odd face. It has no middle ground. The moment I stop smiling, it plunges into murderous grief. So when I'm feeling serene and happy but not actually smiling, people often say, 'Cheer up! It may never happen!' And when I'm going through one of my thin periods (increasingly rare, these days) it's even worse. Then, they even say, 'Cheer up!' when I'm *still smiling*.

So, as you can see, my bloom was never a conspicuous feature of my life. However, I learnt you can do a lot by standing with your back to the light, your collar turned up, and your weight on one leg. It wasn't exactly a substitute for bloom but it got me

125

through Domesday Discos with a minimum of ego damage.

In fact, being with child was probably the nearest I'd ever come to bloom. Although at the antenatal class every week one of my fellow-primagravidas kept saying to me, 'You look tired!' When you're feeling fit and energetic and people say you look tired, it makes you want to turn your collar up, right to the ceiling.

We learnt some useful stuff in those classes, though. One thing we learnt was that the Birth Business was in the grips of a great debate. Deciding to become a mother nowadays is like joining the priesthood during the Counter-Reformation: one seeks a little gentle advice and uncovers a whirlpool of passionate dogma. At the time of which I speak, the Natural Brigade was on the offensive, and the High-Technology Orthodox Medicine Regiment were wheeling about in disarray. In the bad old days, I gathered, men in white coats strapped you down, tied you to drips, drugged you to the eyeballs and induced you in office hours so they wouldn't miss the midnight movie.

But now one is not so inevitably the victim of the drip, the snip, and the electronic monitoring blip. Now one is urged to flee high technology and seek out a Third World hedge in which to give birth, attended by a knitting, singing, kinship system. Or failing that, one should plunge into a darkened paddling pool, preferably in France.

The idea is that birth is a natural process and that you should try and tune in to your body. Your body, apparently, will tell you all you need to know. I had wept, of course, through the Natural Childbirth documentaries on TV: wept enough to fill a wretched paddling pool, but I didn't find this line of argument terribly reassuring. Is Dame Nature infallible? Doesn't she nod off sometimes? And I wasn't sure that I trusted my body as far as I could throw it, i.e. the sofa. My body has told me some outrageous lies in its time. And towards the end of my pregnancy it began to behave strangely, as if it were losing its nerve.

Apart from the tiredness of the first few weeks I had felt remarkably well. But at about the eighth month I began to feel faint if I lay down on my back. It felt as if an elephant was sitting on my chest. Actually, it looked a bit like that, too. One day I came across one of those Test-Your-Fitness-In-The-Street machines. You put in a coin, insert a fingertip, and it tells you whether you're in prime athletic condition, just about average, or aged, sick and debilitated. It said I was dead. At the time, considering how I felt, that seemed like an understatement. Was this the body I was to trust and to which I was to listen? I crossed my fingers. Or, at least, I planned to cross them later, when I felt a little stronger.

But the most distressing of my pregnancy symptoms was not merely painful but socially inconvenient. I shall now dwell on it for a moment or two, especially as it is disgusting. It was colic. Or as they say up North, wind. There was plenty in the baby books about the baby and its colic, but not a mention of the poor pregnant mother, who, shovelling beans and bran down in a desperate attempt to keep the channels open, discovers to her horror that as the baby's head has locked down into her pelvic girdle like a cork in a bottle of ancient port, there is no way out for the gaseous emanations.

I kept waking at 3.30 a.m. with agonizing gripes raking my vast abdomen as a Force 9 gale rampaged around desperate for an exit. At times I quite expected steam to come screaming out of my navel. What's more, I bore these torments alone and in secret as Van Dyke never seemed to be bothered by wind. Indeed, that is part of his charm.

So the problem facing me was, if the magic moment came and I realized that wind would out, how could I achieve this without disturbing the elegant ambience of our lives? On one occasion, I have to record that circumstances obliged me to withdraw from the supper-table, retire to the utility room and avail myself of the cat flap. And, oh dear, how farcical life is sometimes – this was the very moment at which *the cat had decided to come in*. Alas, poor Pussy. I trust she did not misinterpret this as an act of personal malice. She must have been fairly insulted, however, since for several hours afterwards she remained obstinately absent. Gone With The Wind, in fact.

For months I had been wrestling with a novel. I had to get it finished before the birth. But every time I sat down at my desk my mind went whizzing off to the Birth Business. Was my case packed? I checked it a hundred times. Would it really matter that I hadn't done my breathing practice every day and had put on a mighty 40 lb instead of the recommended maximum of 28?

What would happen? Would my body manage? Or would I die? Did people die in childbirth these days? I knew already that by virtue of my great age (i.e. over thirty) I was regarded as a High Risk patient and would have to go to Gloucester, which offered technology and consultants, instead of waddling off to the friendly little local maternity hospital round the corner, as I had hoped.

When would it start? Would I be whisked away in an ambulance with sirens blaring? Would Van Dyke and I get stuck in a blizzard somewhere on the Cotswold escarpment at 3 a.m.? I hoped not. Being born in a rusting Ford Escort was not my idea of a distinguished debut for a bulldog, let alone Old Baby.

What would its first cry be like? What would it

look like? Would it have enough feet, and so on? Would it be OK?

'Are you OK? How are things down there?' I whispered urgently in the loo. I've never spent so much time contemplating my navel – or gained so little Eastern serenity from it. The baby seemed to be on the verge of panic, too. It was enormous. At moments, I am sure, it simultaneously plucked desperately at the roots of my pubic hair and kicked me in the tonsils. It was getting claustrophobic in there.

We visited Gloucester Maternity Hospital for a look around. It seemed very pleasant. I asked if they had a birthing chair. The nurse said they did, and added, 'I thought you looked the type.' Was this an insult? I expect so. But I was too keyed up to care. If only I could run away from it all. By its very nature, though, pregnancy is a cunning condition. However hard you run, you're always running *towards* it.

With such thoughts whirling round my mind it's hardly surprising that my novel proved so dreadfully boring. For once life was more exciting than fiction. I could scarcely force myself to read even the miserable few words I managed each day. And if I got engrossed in the novel-writing business for more than a minute or two, the thunder of tiny heels summoned me back to the real drama about to unfold. The day approached: that date on which Old Baby and I were supposed to do our thing.

The bear-down-by date was 2 February – or, as they call it in shadowy medieval places, Candlemas. I was quite struck by this at first. I liked the idea of a baby born on Candlemas, until I discovered what it meant. Do you know what Candlemas means? It means the Purification of the Blessed Virgin Mary.

How absolutely typical of Christianity. Decreeing that women must be purified after childbirth is bad enough but to demand it of Mary, after all she'd done, and not done, seems downright perverse. If anybody

129

didn't need purifying, surely it was she. Patriarchs! All the same! I bet they didn't let her wear trousers either. So when Candlemas came and went and Old Baby ignored the date and sat tight, I was glad.

A few days later the serene, glowing Candide gave birth – a week earlier than *her* date. Typical. What's more, she managed, without drugs, with just the breathing exercises and one night's labour (from midnight to breakfast), to produce a serene, glowing, Buddha-like daughter, who was duly named after a Dogon village. We went to visit them and as I balanced The Doge precariously on my bump I felt my own baby give her a vigorous kick from below. Jealousy obviously sets in early.

Seeing Candide with her baby only made me feel mine would never come. Everyone else had had theirs, except Sheila and me. We would telephone each other daily with fresh accounts of how we hadn't dramatically gone into labour. Every few days I went to see the consultant who examined me and pronounced me still not ripe. Well, what did they expect in February? I hadn't even got a heated greenhouse. The consultant also suggested that we couldn't go on meeting like this. Well, not for ever.

Then one day I threw my novel into the waste paper basket, ran into what was to be the baby's room, and went bananas. I made a mobile out of artificial flowers and hung it up. Then I made another out of shells, paper birds and silk flowers, and hung it up. Then I made another out of bits of old cream crackers packets and sticking plaster. And so on: on and on.

I strung a giant bamboo pole across the ceiling. I hung ten mobiles from it. I gathered together all the little vests and folded them, ready, in the top drawer. I arranged the many toys we'd been given around the place in attitudes of frozen gaiety.

Van Dyke came into the room and immediately

struck his head on three mobiles, two of them noisy and one quite sharp. He looked at me quizzically. 'You have gone too far.' Mind you, by Dutch standards, that's not all that far.

I went downstairs and started to scrub the hall floor, right up to the front door. The exit: get it? A symbolic propitiation of the gods of entrances and exits – who was it? Oh yes – Janus. Although we were, by now, already more than halfway through February. I had missed Janus. I'd missed Candlemas. I'd missed St Valentine's, patron saint of lovers. At this rate I was going to miss Midsummer.

And then Candide arrived with her husband. She was carrying the serene baby and he was carrying the hottest take-away curry available in Gloucestershire. Even as he stepped across the threshold the paper bag began to smoulder. 'Come on, Sue!' they cried. 'If this doesn't do the trick, nothing ever will!' It was the night of 17 February. The eve of John Ruskin's birthday. The patron saint, if one might put it like that, of little girls.

Chapter 13

All that night I lay awake as rather exciting spasms of pain came and went. Was I in labour? Or was it just the curry? Was this really *it*? I was sure it was. I got up at 6.30 p.m. and had a cup of hot chocolate and an enormous sandwich. But then the pains stopped. This was disappointing. After all, we were sixteen days past the estimated date of confinement. Would I have to be induced? And how did they induce you, anyway? I had heard rumours of drips and of the breaking of waters and it all sounded rather cataclysmic. Wouldn't it be better just to put a saucer of milk at the bottom of the bed?

'Come on, Old Baby,' I urged it. 'Look at the lovely world waiting for you.' The first rays of sunlight were just creeping across the snow.

'Don't be frightened,' I whispered, trying to ignore my own palpitating heart. 'It's all right out here in the world. And there are doughnuts and dolphins and other treats waiting for you.' The baby was unnaturally still for a moment: pretending it was asleep, no doubt.

I had a routine appointment that morning at Gloucester Hospital, and I was pretty sure that I was leaking amniotic fluid, in tiny quantities, now and then. In all the birth-sagas I'd heard the waters broke dramatically, soaking beds and flooding floors. Not mine. But I had an odd feeling, rather like being in the bath and gradually sensing that the plug doesn't fit very well and that bit by bit you're losing the bathwater. Was something stirring? Perhaps they would decide to keep me in. I lumbered out to the car. It took us twenty minutes to scrape the frost off the windows. What a good job I wasn't an emergency.

I was filled with a precarious sense of wellbeing as we drove down into the Severn plain to Gloucester. On either side the steep fields and hanging woods lay snow-struck and glittered in the sunlight. I wondered if this day of immaculate frosts and flawless skies was to be the day on which, at last, I'd meet the creature who had trundled about inside me for so long. I also wondered, fleetingly, if it would be my last day on earth. I wasn't fluttery with panic: my fear was huge, deep-frozen.

At Gloucester the consultant and his acolytes agreed that I still wasn't ripe. 'But I think I'm losing amniotic fluid,' I told them. 'What do you think?' They had another brief look.

'No, I don't think so,' he smiled. 'Probably just a bit of urine leaking. Go home for a couple of days and come and see us again on Wednesday.'

I escaped with a mixture of relief and irritation, like when you leave the dentist's but know you've got a worse appointment to come. I was glad they weren't desperate to induce me. I liked their willingness to let me come along at my own speed. But on the other hand, I was increasingly convinced . . . yes! There it was again! Isn't it annoying when male doctors think that their female patients don't know whether they're urinating or not? I mean, they know when they're peeing, don't they? So did I. Ah well. We drove back, a feeling of anticlimax hanging over

133

us, my hospital case unopened on the back seat.

Back home, I was sure I had sprung a leak. Not
wishing to be fobbed off again, I collected a sample of
the stuff and carried it round the corner to the
friendly little local maternity hospital where the
lucky under-thirty-year-olds gave birth. My speci-
men looked like washing-up water with little bits of
coconut floating about in it. What were the bits of
coconut? Bits of baby? Was the baby ... *breaking up
in there?* Was I losing the baby with the bathwater?
Horrors!

A Welsh midwife tested my sample and pronounced it the Real Thing. She rang up Gloucester
Hospital and understandably exulted a bit, given the
size and seniority of Gloucester and the modesty of
her own establishment.

'Mrs Limb, whom you saw this morning, is here,
and she's got a *whole pot* of amniotic fluid!, she
scolded them. Then she turned to me. 'They want
you to go back in.'

The snow-covered fields were still sparkling,
etcetera, but the charm of the landscape was beginning to pall. We did not talk much. I'd made sure Van
Dyke had a chocolate bar with him, as recommended
by Jane Fonda, so that he wouldn't faint later at an inconvenient moment. But we'd eaten it long before
we'd passed the first of the wintry woods. Deep
dread, and an almost joyous excitement, alternated in
my heart. Soon I would meet Old Baby, face to face!
The next twenty-four hours might be absolute hell,
but by this time tomorrow it was almost sure to be all
over.

Please let the baby be all right, I prayed. *I'm sorry
about all that stuff about Candlemas. And the Annun-
ciation. All right, kill me: I'm a blasphemous wretch, I
deserve it, but let the baby live.*

When I got out of the car I felt different: as if the
baby's head had locked into a kind of ring of bone just

above the top of my legs. It hurt when I moved. I had to walk with my legs wide apart. Was this a good sign? It was certainly far from stylish. I felt like a piece of 1950s furniture.

We were ushered into a room where I managed to put a brave face on it for a couple of seconds as I was examined by a midwife, then a young doctor, then another doctor who looked slightly insane in a John Cleese sort of way. Each time they brought in a new trolley complete with a whole new examination-kit on it, all wrapped in carefully sterile packages. I could practically hear the pounds clocking up. Thank goodness this was paid for by what remained of the National Health Service, I thought. Although this was not a conviction that persisted for very long.

'Well,' announced the slightly insane-looking doctor, rubbing his hand in an unnerving way, 'your cervix is still very unripe, but we've decided to plough on.' *Plough on?* I tried to get up off the bed.

'It's all right,' I blustered. 'Why don't I just go home for a couple more days . . .' But he had gone, and the midwife was busy setting up the drip.

She was a plump, relaxed girl called Tessa. I turned to her with a pathetic need for help, support, and, I now realize, mother-love. She was from South Wales. All midwives come from South Wales, it seems. I suppose it's the female equivalent of mining. I made friends furiously with Tessa but gathered that she would be going off-duty in a couple of hours. And not only that: she was going out of the room, right now! Yes, she'd gone! Help! I turned to Van Dyke and gave him a synthetic smile. He wasn't fooled.

The drip went into my hand. You could see the stuff slipping down the tube. I felt somehow rather sorry for my hand with this thing strapped to its vein. And then there was the belt round my enormous belly recording the baby's heartbeat. Next to the bed was what looked like a computer, showing the infant's pulse rate. 140 was about normal, they said. There were also a lot of other figures that flashed and changed. What did they represent? Degree of dread? Amount of take-away curry still in the system? We joked nervously.

The drip was operating very slowly at the moment but apparently they'd gradually turn it up so that sooner or later my veins would be flooded with the stuff. What was it called? Oxytoxycytopoxin? Or was that a rock band? Whatever it was called, it was supposed to ease me into labour gently just like Dame Nature. What actually happened was that I had no pains at all for an hour and a half and then, suddenly, a contraction every three minutes.

This couldn't be right. This wasn't Dame Nature's way, surely. She starts the business with gradual twinges every twenty minutes or so, so you have time to get used to the idea, to catch up on your correspondence and make 10 lb of marmalade. Whereas Oxytoxycytopoxin didn't leave me even a spare moment to curse Van Dyke.

I was beginning to think Oxytoxycytopoxin was another of those Aztec gods. The God of Misogyny, maybe. My contractions registered on the computer print-out like a map of the Himalayas, only steeper. The medics came in now and then, studied the printout, and said that that was more like it. After two and half hours of pains every three minutes I got desperate. *Never mind the damned print-out, I thought. What about me? What about my baby? It can't be doing us any good, going through this every three* – oh look out, another's coming – oh help, here we go – now which shall I do? Deep breathing, shallow breathing or quick panting?

I was completely confused. I didn't know where I was in the birth process. Having pains every three minutes belongs to the later stages of labour surely. Not the first bit. How much longer would I have to go on like this? The next time a midwife came in I seized her.

'Gas and air!' I croaked. 'Can I have some gas and air?'

'Good heavens, no!' she breezed. 'You're not nearly far enough on for that.'

She was a stranger. Welsh Tessa had gone off duty and despite promises to look in on me tomorrow and find out how it had gone, she had in fact vanished out of my life for ever. She had been replaced by a coarse-featured bully of a woman. Isn't it odd how everybody who works in a hospital is either an angel or a monster of cruelty? Couldn't I even have gas and air? I felt as though some frail thread upon which I had been hanging had snapped. A gentle smile! A kind word! A hint of understanding, *please*.

The next contraction closed like a wave over my head and through it I saw her bustle off. I felt too weak, frightened and demoralized to argue. Nobody seemed to have any time to help and support us as we faced this extraordinary series of paroxysms. Already the institution was making me feel weedy and apologetic, quite apart from the physical endurance I needed to ride the waves of pain.

I surfaced from the contraction and was about to swear feebly at Van Dyke when the electronic blip registering the baby's heartbeat slowed dramatically from 140 to somewhere around 70. We both froze in horror. Was our baby going? The little blip sound hesitated, almost stopped. The pen recording the print-out slewed, and did some crazed disconnected scratchy little marks, totally unlike anything we'd seen before.

'Oh God! Oh God! The baby!' Van Dyke raced out of the room to fetch help.

'Hang on!' I cried to my unreachable child. 'Please, Old Baby! Hang on! Don't die!' Tears jammed my eyes, ears, nose and throat. Van Dyke stormed in with the midwife who banged an oxygen mask on to my face with what seemed like scarcely concealed panic.

'Breathe deeply!' she commanded. 'We were bringing you on a bit too quickly.' While she turned down the drip I breathed away for dear life – for very dear life, not my own. We all watched the blip and the magic number which kept flashing and changing. 76.82.84. Thank God! It was climbing. 77. Oh no! It had dropped again.

'Don't die, my baby,' I willed it. 'Don't die.' Slowly the baby's heartbeat climbed back to normal.

As for my heart, it was bursting. I didn't trust myself to speak – even if I could have, with the oxygen mask crammed firmly on to my face. I didn't trust myself to think. The most frightening thing was the way the medics reacted. They didn't seem able to hide their concern. The slightly insane-looking doctor burst in, had a cursory glance at me, mere body that I was, and closely studied the damned print-out. At the place where the baby's heart had suddenly slowed the line of peaks had exploded into a scattered flight of birds.

'We'll give you an epidural,' he announced, 'take you off the drip, give you a bit of a rest.' And he ran off. Whatever next? Did they know what they were doing? *Give me a bit of a rest?* What was this, science? First they administer a severe shock to your system and then they think the better of it.

I was wheeled into another room. Van Dyke was still at my side. I clung to his hand so hard a weaker man would have heard his finger bones crack. But Van Dyke's were strengthened by decades of arpeggios. He was feeling utterly powerless, of course. But the mere fact of his being there, amongst this bungling and blundering, was the only thing that kept me on the right side of the abyss. I kept breathing the oxygen and willing it to go to my baby

138

and help it. Its heartbeat slowed again, and then steadied back to normal.

I was allowed to stop breathing the oxygen. A harassed-looking anaesthetist appeared. He was absurdly handsome and reminded me of an old friend of mine, Michael Doyle, who organizes large parts of the Edinburgh Festival. It all began to seem like a dream. Was this guy Michael or not? Was I hallucinating? Were these my last moments on earth?

'What do you know about epidurals?' he asked, with the nearest thing to a human smile I had seen for hours. I opened my mouth to answer, but even as I began to speak another man came up, plucked the anaesthetist by the sleeve and took him aside for a whispered consultation.

'There's a woman ... and then ... and as for this woman ...' At this point he glanced at me and became aware of Van Dyke's most wintry stare fixed upon him. He went into double-double whisper as he discussed my case. Of course, the patient must never be allowed to know what's going on. Their mystery, their wretched mystery.

Well, when I say *discussed*, no more than ten seconds seemed to be necessary; then they both charged off without a word of explanation. Disorientated and desperate, all we could do was watch the regular blip of our baby's life and will it to go on. *Don't stop, little clock*, I thought to it. *Don't stop. Your day is just beginning.* In the world outside it was apparently 11.30 p.m. Good heavens! I'd thought it was about 6. These closed grey rooms, with their sterile windowless gleam, destroy all sense of being in touch with sun and moon.

Our midwife bustled in. She looked, if possible, even more bored and unfriendly. 'You're having a Caesarian,' she announced. 'I'm going to shave you and give you a catheter.'

'What happened to the anaesthetist?' I asked. 'Can

I still have my epidural? I want to be conscious. I want to see the baby and—'

'No time for that,' she snapped. 'You're having a general anaesthetic. You're an emergency, dear.' That *dear* was particularly hard to bear. She then turned to another nurse somewhere in the vicinity.

'I hope they're not expecting me to do theatre,' she complained. 'I shall be really fed up if I have to . . . *again*.'

Terrific, wasn't it? Terrifically confidence-inspiring. Terrifically reassuring. But wait. Worse was to come. Duly shaved, and with yet another tube attached to my mystified old body, I was wheeled somewhere else. It was all lights and grey metal surfaces. Van Dyke had disappeared. I was on my own now. A profound fatalism rose from my bowels and stilled me.

The same anaesthetist appeared, looking rather embarrassed. He made no mention of epidurals, but briefly told me that he was about to administer the general anaesthetic. Halfway through his speech we were deafened by a burst of raucous laughter from someone at a nearby sink.

'Stop that noise over there!' he snapped. Then he placed the mask on my face. It felt cold and smelt of rubber. I sensed his attention was elsewhere: he was looking round anxiously.

'Where's the surgeon?' he called, with every appearance of alarm. 'Where's the surgeon?'

His face suddenly started to revolve like a firework, and then it soared away from me into the ceiling. Gratefully I surrendered myself into unconsciousness. O give me the dark, I yearned. Never mind the pain and the anguish. I can't bear any more *muddle*. The blackness came. It was like being sucked upwards into a plughole, out of life. I wonder if dying is a bit like that? And in a sense this was a death, too the death of my old self. Youth, carelessness and selfish pleasure all went whirling away upwards and into the black shredder. I had to hang in a void while they lifted the small new creature out into the light. Poor baby! Alone so soon.

They had told Van Dyke to wait in the waiting room. Fathers were not allowed to watch Caesarians when a general anaesthetic was used. 'The baby will be out very soon,' they promised him. 'In about ten minutes or so. We'll bring it straight to you.' An hour and a half later Van Dyke was still waiting in the waiting room. Nobody had come to tell him anything.

Then a nurse seemed to notice him, en passant, stuck her head round the door, and said, 'Do you know what you've got?'

'What do you mean?' asked poor Van Dyke, struggling with the awful pitfalls of idiomatic English. What you've got? It sounds like a disease, for God's sake.

'You've got a daughter,' the nurse went on. 'She's in Special Care, because she had breathing difficulties and she was a funny colour. Your wife's just coming out of the anaesthetic now. You can come and see her.'

Yes. I was coming out of the anaesthetic. I seemed to be lying on my side. A patch of grey wall appeared in my vision and for a moment it was just wall, and I was nothing, nobody, just a sense: seeing.

'You've got a porky little daughter,' said a voice close to my ear. I recognized the bored, impatient tone of the midwife. Wasn't it time she went off-duty? Wasn't it time she went off-duty – for ever? A porky little daughter. These were the words which conveyed to me the most precious message of my life.

I didn't dare to move. My body seemed held together with little more than skin. The bones and muscles weren't working any more. All the same, I managed to sidle my eyes up sideways, far enough to see the midwife's face. Porky? I thought, surveying her snout and large pendulous cheeks. Porky? You can talk – *dear*.

'She's in Special Care,' she went on, in a matter-of-fact voice. 'She's had breathing difficulties and she was a funny colour.'

Then I was wheeled off somewhere. Still half-conscious, my brain struggled to master the situation. A funny colour? What did they mean? I didn't remember anything about colour in the baby books. And breathing difficulties sounded bad. I knew how important breathing was for babies. Where was the Special Care place? And where was I? How near to it?

But I was in nowhere land, tied down by more tubes than ever, unable to move, and with reality constantly slipping away and then suddenly jerking back. I registered that I was in a small room. It was fairly dark and felt mercifully private. I seemed to be alone, Indeed, Caesarians had a room to themselves.

'Hello, Sue,' Van Dyke's voice was at my ear. 'The baby's in Special Care. She's got some breathing problems and they said she was a funny kolour.' I wanted to hear this message again. What did it mean? What breathing problems? What colour? What was wrong? What were her chances? Van Dyke couldn't help. They'd told him no more than they'd told me.

We waited, in our room, through the remote watches of the night. 2 a.m., 3 a.m. No news came. Was no news bad news?

I stared at the wall. I don't think we talked much, except to speculate about what might be wrong, and to reassure each other, with a painfully transparent optimism, that it must be all right, really.

No one came, no one disturbed our vigil. Then suddenly at 4 a.m. the door to our room burst open and a burly ward sister bustled in. My goodness, she was frightening. So that's what *battleaxe* means when applied to middle-aged women. One glance from her was enough to cut off your circulation.

'You must go home now,' she barked at Van Dyke, 'and let your wife get some sleep!' As if Van Dyke was wilfully keeping me awake with a series of songs, dances and jokes. As if I *could* sleep, having lost contact with my baby and not met her yet. The fearsome lady was obviously used to being obeyed without question. But Van Dyke stood his ground. Excellent Dutch! Their democratic history paid off now. The Dutch have always hated tyrants.

'But what about our baby?' he asked. 'How is she? We haven't seen her. Nobody has told us anything. Ij'm not going till I've seen her.' Well done, Van Dyke! I silently applauded, while at the same time cringing lest the battleaxe be stung by this defiance into worse fierceness. She wasn't, though. She even softened slightly – say, from steel to aluminium.

'Oh!' she exclaimed. 'Haven't you seen her? Nurse will take you down. And you, Mrs Limb – get some rest!' What did she expect me to do? With a catheter in my bladder, a wound drain in my wound, a drip in my wrist, a great deal of anaesthetic still furring up my brain, and post-operative shock and post-natal incredulity weighing me down, I was hardly likely to tuck up my drips and skip off in search of Gloucester's nightlife. I groaned slightly as she bustled importantly out, and I wish now I had shrieked aloud.

Van Dyke was gone for what seemed like months. My imagination got jumpy and began to play some strange tricks. Why was he away so long? Was anything wrong? There could only be one explanation: the baby was dead. That's why it was taking so long. Yes. They'd told him. It was taking some time to get over the shock, but soon he'd come in and lie to me that it was all OK. They'd tell me the truth when I was stronger. Any minute now he'd come in and tell me that he'd seen the baby and that she was O.K.

'Ij've seen the baby, and she is wonderful!' he cried, rushing in. 'Ij held her in my arms! She's completely O.K. The breathing problem was caused by some amniotic fluid which she'd swallowed, but she's brought it up now and she's fine. They say they'll bring her up to you soon. Look! Here's a photo they took of her. Ij'll have to go now. See you tomorrow, darling.'

After he'd gone, I stared at the photo. An immensely fat baby lay fast asleep, looking indeed rather like a sucking pig. But on the other hand, looking a bit like my brother. Soon I would see her. My pulse raced in anticipation. I couldn't wait. But it seemed I would have to.

In the depths of the night, two black nurses materialized at my bedside. 'Have you brought my baby?' I croaked.

'No, dear, we've come to wash you,' they murmured. Slowly and gently they sponged me, hardly saying anything; their voices, when they spoke, fluttering softly about the room like nocturnal birds. I gave myself up to their ministrations. They were gentle, but somehow detached. Just what I needed: a moment of peace in the midst of the nightmare. They took my old sheets away. They seemed to be covered with blood.

4.30 a.m., 5 a.m., 6 a.m. . . . It was six hours since she'd been born. Surely, if she was OK, they'd have brought her to me by now? After all, wasn't it vitally important for the mother and the baby to be together immediately after birth if possible? The terrible dread crept back over me. 7.30.

Daylight came: a rather dirty grey daylight. My wound began to ache. Whenever I moved, I felt cut in half. I couldn't believe in the reality of my baby. She'd been living an independent life for eight hours, it seemed. Had she been fed? Was she all right? Wasn't she lonely, puzzled and deeply shocked by her new life? Why wasn't she here by my side? How could they possibly be this cruel? She must either be

144

dead or very ill. There was no other explanation.

8 o'clock. Not a nurse in sight. Had the government cuts removed the last shreds of medical help? 9 o'clock. Miracle! A nurse appeared.

'Where's my baby?' I cried. 'I haven't even seen her yet!

'Oh, haven't you?' she sounded surprised. 'I'll go and phone Special Care.'

About twenty minutes later she popped her head round the door. 'Sorry! They're a bit too busy to bring her up. But if you think you can get in a wheelchair, we could take you down.'

Get into a wheelchair? I can't convey how impossible this was. It would be days before I could even raise an eyebrow. And even then I'd need a block and tackle.

When she'd gone, the tears took over. I couldn't move. I couldn't even protest. The offer of a wheelchair was, I began to see, a cunning trick to give me a little hope that my baby was still alive. 10 o'clock. 11 o'clock. The morning unfolded endlessly. Outside my window was a hospital wall and beyond it I sensed a street where a pneumatic drill roared for hour after hour. The snow had turned to slush. The world was a terrible place.

Back in Stroud, I knew, Van Dyke was catching up on his sleep. So I couldn't expect him to visit me till the afternoon. Footsteps passed in the corridor outside my lonely cell. Nobody came. Of course. They were all avoiding me. The woman who'd lost her baby, poor thing.

By 11.30 I had lost all hope. I gazed at the photograph through torrents of tears.

'Is that really you?' I asked. 'Are you really there?' There was no answer. The telepathy of pregnancy was gone, and in its place nothing but a howling silence.

At midday, twelve hours exactly after my deliv-

145

ery, a nurse threw open my door. 'You've got a visitor,' she grinned.

I scowled up from my wet pillow. A visitor was the last thing I needed. *Go away, whoever you are,* I thought. *Get lost. I can't face you.* Then the nurse wheeled in a transparent fishtank-like cot, and asleep inside it was my visitor. *Baby Limb,* said a label, 9 lb 5½ oz. She was alive! And she was pink!

I stared into the fishtank. She lay on her side, her eyes closed. Her nose was indeed snout-like. She was well-upholstered, too: her tiny arms, folded in front of her, were like eiderdowns. On her brow I could see small star-shaped wrinkles, just like Van Dyke's mother. She moved her fingers slightly, scratched her face and woke herself up. A pair of huge, flaring, wide-apart eyes opened, and she fixed me with a dark scowl. Could she see my face through her perspex cot? Did she know it was me? Could she possibly sense what a mother was, and want hers? Had she missed me in those twelve endless hours? Had she been lonely?

I'd missed her first cry, and her second cry, and all the cries since. She'd been given two bottles of milk, down there in Special Care, because they were 'too busy' to bring her up to me. How long did it take to give a baby a bottle? A hell of a lot longer than it takes to wheel a cot twenty yards, take it up one floor in a lift, wheel it another twenty yards, and then lift the baby on to the waiting breast. But all bitterness melted now, as her dark eyes registered the light, her small stomach signalled hunger, and her mouth opened like a baby bird's.

'Laaaaaar!' she cried. 'Laaaaaaar!' A deep, plaintive, melancholy call, like a seabird lost in a fog.

Chapter 14

Let us draw a veil over the next five days, permitting ourselves only a twitch and a glimpse. The hospital practised 'rooming in', which meant that the baby was in her cot at my side twenty-four hours a day, and it was my job to take care of her. As I had waited in anguish for her for so long, it may seem odd to carp at this enlightened idea. But a Caesarian requires bedrest for a fortnight afterwards, and lifting heavy objects after abdominal surgery is the worst thing you can do.

Now this baby was a heavy object by anybody's standards. I was further hampered by my drip, catheter and wound drain. And when the baby started to be sick in her cot, and turned her face upwards to gasp for help, and I had to try and lift her out and stop her choking and ring the bell all at once, I ended up like a frantic marionette with its wires in a twist and its stuffing coming out.

To my horror I discovered there was a No Solid Food rule for several days after a Caesarian. This was to do with combating the post-operative wind, which had blown me up to almost pregnant proportions again.

'No solid food until the bowels are back to normal,' gleamed a nurse in steely glasses. I groaned. I knew my bowels of old. It would take a truckload of turnip-tops to get the bastards back into anything like normal service.

'Give me bran!' I pleaded. But all I got was a tiny square of ice cream, the size of a box of matches. Nutritionally, of course, the box of matches itself would have made much more sense.

Fibre was forbidden. They knew best, *Ice cream only for two days. Then on the third day, a suppository and you will rise from the dead.* Well, long before that I rose to the goddam ceiling, borne up by my vast belly, and hovered over Gloucestershire like the Cloud of Unknowing. On the third day, up went the suppository and out came a typhoon, blowing the hospital sky-high and causing millions of dollars' worth of damage on distant Australian beaches. A voice spoke out of the whirlwind: 'Give this woman some food.' But nobody heard.

Then there were the nights. Rooming in means that if your own baby isn't keeping you awake, someone else's is. Their cries were all so different: 'Akakaka-kakakak!' 'Hecate! Hecate!' 'Whacker! Whacker!' And of course, melodious and near at hand: 'Laaaaar! Laaaaar!' But this variety of human cry was only fascinating for the first hour of the first night. Thereafter it became more and more of a maddening cacophony.

Halfway through the fourth sleepless night I realized I was probably clinically insane by now: what the upper classes call absolutely barking. But since I was dying of starvation and fatigue it didn't really seem to matter. By the fifth day, my head had stopped being a head and had become a belfry: from the neck up I was all pigeon shit and crumbling stonework. From the neck down I was an abyss.

'You're looking much better today,' beamed a

nurse perkily, jolting my corpse into a sitting position and plumping up the pillows behind me.

'Yes. I'm hoping to go back to Stroud today,' I rattled. 'To Stroud Maternity Hospital, you know. It's just round the corner from where I live . . .' But she had gone.

Now, I had to make a massive effort today. Though I had not eaten or slept for five days, and though I knew privately that I was dead and mad, to the casual observer I had made some progress: I had discarded my drip, wound drain and catheter. I could even manage the three yards to the loo, holding on to the wall, of course – if I set out after what should have been breakfast, I could make it there and back by lunchtime, as it was probably still known out there in the free world. If only I could persuade the powers that be to let me go back to Stroud! I sat on the edge of my bed and tried to look alive.

They said I could go! I leapt up and got dressed so fast I got a severe attack of fireflies-before-the-eyes and fire-alarm-in-the-ears.

'Come on!' I gasped to Van Dyke, who had appeared with the old French carrycot held together with bulldog clips. 'Let's get out of here!' We had to wait for our escort, though. A nurse had to carry the baby out in case we dropped her and sued them. For one wild moment I considered asking her to carry me too. Limping towards the daylight of escape, however, I took heart, and even thought of stopping at the desk to thank them – er, well, to say goodbye . . . at the very least, to register our departure. But the shift had changed again and two complete strangers watched us pass.

So we left the vast modern gleam of Gloucester and presented ourselves at Stroud Maternity Hospital. It looks like a low-budget wartime building: small, scruffy, one-storey. Unpretentious, to put it mildly, but surrounded by a field and with a couple of horses

149

nearby. We were welcomed with an enormous Sisterly smile. 'Is this your baby? Isn't she *lovely*? What are you calling her?'

We were calling her Beatrice. It was nearly the name of the Dutch Queen, and definitely the name of my favourite Shakespearean heroine – the Beatrice in *Much Ado About Nothing*. This lady's merry quips have long delighted me. 'I had rather hear my dog bark at a crow than a man say he loves me,' she says. That's the stuff. The baby Beatrice did not enjoy the full glory of her name for long, however. Before she was a day old I had already begun to think of her as Beano. Beano Van Dyke. Weird, isn't it? Still, at least it's vegetarian.

'Beatrice!' exclaimed the Sister, cuddling her. 'That's different! Well, come and see your bed, Mrs Limb. And make yourself at home.'

Bed! Never was the word more welcome. It was in a corner of the only ward (divided into two: four beds in each), and equipped with curtains I could draw around me for privacy. The curtains were scattered with a pattern of huge red roses. I sank into this bed of roses with a deep sigh. Beano was changed into another backless hospital nightie and installed in the inevitable fishtank at my side. She opened her huge eyes and stared at the roses on the curtains. She had never seen chintz before.

Almost immediately a midwife appeared. She was, of course, from South Wales: a short, neat, middle-aged body whom I had met at the antenatal classes. She reminded me of an old-fashioned primary school headmistress with her dignity and air of reined-in fierceness.

'How are you gettin' on with the feedin', Mrs Limb?' she inquired. I was amazed. It was the first time anyone had asked me how I was getting on – at least, in a way that invited a serious answer. However, I wasn't sure that I was getting on all that well. I knew that babies could be expected to suck for, say, ten or fifteen minutes a side, but that one should work up to that gradually. But Beano seemed to want to go on and on: half an hour on one breast alone was not unusual.

This was another reason for my sleepless nights. Why she behaved like this was a mystery. I knew I had plenty of milk because it had 'come in' bang on schedule – I had awoken on the appointed day to find myself in the Peak District. Perhaps she was reluctant to let go now because of our unfortunate separation at the beginning, clinging on by the skin of her gums to anything that might be a mother.

'I think I've got sore nipples,' I conjectured, never one to let a possible ailment escape.

'They don't look sore to me,' said the midwife. 'I don't think she's goin' on properly.' She seized Beano, made her mouth gape wide, and then banged her onto me with a crocodilian bite. Immediately things began to go better. I felt much more like a cow. Any minute now I would rub my innocent behind against a tree.

The midwife stayed with us for twenty minutes, asking me how everything else had gone, watching Beano perform, and dispensing shrewd advice of a reassuringly antiquated sort. Hot flannels, etc, etc, etc. I can't quite remember now what I was supposed to do with them, but it sounded wonderfully pictur-esque at the time.

By the time the midwife left my side, the baby had completed her feed and gone to sleep. I'd been given *twenty minutes of undivided attention*. I drew back my curtains and smiled at the world.

Dinner time came. A table was set in the middle of the ward, between our four beds. It was cosy and convivial. The dinner ladies pushed in their trolley with hoots of laughter.

'It's only ham and salad I'm afraid, dearr,' said one,

151

with the comforting Gloucestershire double RR, and placed a technicolour plate in front of me. I gazed at it with rapture, like a nineteenth-century explorer surveying an exotic and unexplored part of Africa. The tomatoes were cut in rosettes! Such finesse!

'Would you like coleslaw with your salad, dearr?' she asked. 'Or grated cheese? Or bread and butterr? Or potato salad?'

'Yes, yes, yes and yes, please.'

'Ah, you must've come from Gloucesterr!' she beamed. 'Been starvin' you, 'ave they? Give 'er another dollop of potato salad, Mabel.' These good souls fed us with maternal care and many a joke. Jokes! I'd forgotten they existed.

That evening, when Matron (or was it Sister? Or was it Big Sister? I never did get the hang of the hospital hierarchy) came in to see us all and settle us down for the night, I almost expected her to tuck me in with my teddy and a goodnight story.

'We believe in mothering the mother,' she explained in a slow, quiet North Country voice, soothing enough to make me feel distinctly dozy.

At bedtime Beano was wheeled out in her fishtank to the nursery with all the other babies. Part of the mothering-the-mother system was ensuring that the mothers got some sleep. In the night, they assured us, they would come and wake us individually when our babies needed feeding. So in an exquisite silence I sank down, at last, fathom deep into the shoals of sleep.

In the middle of the night I was awoken by a whisper. 'Mrs Limb? Will you come and feed your baby, please?' I didn't mind being disturbed. I heaved myself out of the warm nest and put on my dressing gown with a sense of wonder, above all: wonder that I'd been asleep for four hours. Four hours! It seemed like a miracle. Sitting in the near-darkness of the nursery, surrounded by other babies sleeping in their cots, I examined my own as she sucked.

In the cosy and kindly atmosphere of Stroud I was rested enough to get to know Beano properly for the first time. Soon I knew it all by heart: the star-shaped wrinkles on her brow, just like her Dutch grandma, the tiny snout, the huge, wide-set eyebrowless eyes, the supernaturally pointed ears, which, I now noticed for the first time, were adorned with dark fur all along their edges. Furry ears! Was she a changeling?

She must be a changeling. How could such a delicious creature be related to such a vile old bag as myself? I noticed she had a tiny patch of hair at the back of her neck: a secret thicket. It was a nice modest brown colour. When she looked up at me her breath was all strawberries. I held mine. To breathe into her face seemed like sacrilege.

I wasn't really prepared for mother love. I'd read so many accounts of maternal indifference: the depression that can set in; the difficulty in relating to the new baby. Knowing how unmaternal I had always been, I'd assumed I'd go that way. My first glimpse of my daughter had been a strange surprise: almost embarrassing, as meeting any stranger is, for the first few moments, embarrassing. I could see very well that she was not what you'd call beautiful. All the same, when she cried her deep soulful cry, I was filled not merely with panic but with passion. I loved her even more for not being beautiful.

But was she comfortable? Were those sunbeams perhaps a little too strong? Did they cause her a moment's inconvenience? I would smash the sun to smithereens if they did. It would be the work of a moment: nothing easier. I would weep tears of anguish the while. There seemed to be lots of anguish about. I only had to imagine her suffering anything at the hands of anybody and I sprouted claws and fangs. I would tear her assailants limb from limb. Motherhood seemed to have turned me, overnight, into a sabre-toothed tiger.

I was more of a sheep than a sabre-toothed tiger, though, when it came to the baby's bathtime. We had to bath our babes according to a rota – it was rather like school. Every day, virtually, a nurse would demonstrate the art, but I never got the hang of it. Beano hated soap and water at first and would shriek with rage as I struggled to avoid drowning us both. I made a secret vow to bath her again, once we got home. My own baths, however, were voluptuous.

The bathrooms were pleasant places to lie and dream in. Every room in the place had a different green hill to look at through the window, lightly scattered sometimes with snow. But then, life was just somehow all right, here. For breakfast we were offered not only All-Bran but extra bran. As much as we could eat. There was always someone to ask, and the staff seemed prepared to spend hours helping people. I lay there in my rosy bower in the corner and stared out at the frosty landscape with an exquisite sense of relief. Perhaps I had died, and this was heaven.

No, it couldn't be heaven. It was too female an institution: run by wise women. Not a consultant in sight. I realized I'd better enjoy it while I could, before the Powers That Be decided to close it. Flurries of snow whirled playfully outside the windows, but next to my bed was a radiator and a warm baby nuzzled and snoozed in my arms. Since we had come to Stroud she had settled down into a steady routine of sleeping and sucking. 'Does your baby ever cry?' asked another mother. 'We never hear her.' I felt stupidly proud of this, as if she had showed exceptional talent. Another of motherhood's eccentric whelms of feeling. Murderous protectiveness, and absurd pride.

Though what exactly *motherhood* meant was still

154

a mystery. The six days at Gloucester had been such a physical ordeal that it had been hard to drag myself beyond the veil of pain, exhaustion and self-pity to contemplate the baby and come to the realization that she was mine: not only mine to glory in, but mine to care for, deal with, protect and nourish. Now, in this pleasant little hospital, I was just as far from coming to terms with it all. Now I basked in the comforts of sleep, food and obedience. I strolled down the corridor without clinging to the walls or feeling faint. A sense of simple animal pleasure in being alive was returning. I was getting better.

So when my own doctor dropped in to see me I managed to be quite chirpy. Right, she said, you can go home tomorrow. Home tomorrow! I thought. How lovely. Most of all I wanted to go home. Of course I did. And yet ... a faint quiver of foreboding ran through me. I looked at Beano, asleep in her fishtank. Or rather – not asleep, but watching me intently without comment. What was she planning?

'Little angel, isn't she?' remarked a passing nurse. 'She's saving it up for when she gets home.' And she gave a merry laugh; which echoed, it seemed to me, somewhat sinisterly among the rose curtains. It was time to draw back those curtains, at last. What on earth lay beyond? I didn't dare look.

Chapter 15

Beano arrived home in a moment of mild weather amidst the snows. The road was streaked with mud. The overhanging evergreens dripped upon the French carrycot. The earth smelt of earth. It was a trailer for spring – or so we thought. Little did we suspect that in Beano's first year of life, we were to be confronted not only with no spring worth mentioning, but no summer at all. Luckily she was too young to realize what she was missing. But this moment of mildness, at the time, seemed like a special dispensation, a gentle gesture from the gods that punishment was over and growth could begin. Ironical, really.

But let me first record the shameful way I behaved as soon as we got home. For a start, I took to my bed, though I suppose I was officially entitled to another three or four days' bedrest. Beano was put into Winnie Windbreaker's wickerwork cot at my side. My mother had cut up an old sheet into six tiny sheets, and done the same to a blanket, so the baby was cosy enough. Just as well, for the blasts of February had returned and the huge pine tree outside our window was weighed down with snow. Frost gripped Gloucestershire again just at the very moment when fear seized my heart.

'Van Dyke!' I cried in horror, as he came in, carrying a tray of cheese sandwiches, gherkins and hot chocolate.

'What ijs it? Ijs the babje all right? Ijs it your wound? Or have you just remembered you've left something in the hospital?'

'That's just it! I've left the nurses in the hospital!'

'Ja, now it ijs just you and me,' affirmed Van Dyke, tucking into the first cheese sandwich. He didn't seem half as scared as I was. Was it Baltic sangfroid? Or was he just fathering the mother? And who was going to father the father? Thank goodness a midwife was going to visit us every day for the first few days. But however could we get through the next sixteen hours until she was due?

'Laaaaar?' inquired Beano.

'Help!' I cried. 'Change her nappy! They say you must involve the father! Go on!' Van Dyke changed the nappy, telling Beano how beautiful she was, and eating his cheese sandwich the while.

'What colour is it?' I hissed.

'Ijs what?'

'What colour's her *poo*, you fool! Is it green?' Van Dyke stared closely at the nappy.

'No,' he concluded. 'It ijs more like French mustard.'

'Thank God.' No diarrhoea – yet. How long would it be before she developed some really serious symptoms?

'LaaaaaAAAAAAAR?'

'She's still crying! Oh, God! What's wrong?

'Ij think she ijs hungry.' Van Dyke laid her onto my breast. She gave me a quick, contemptuous glance and dived into her dinner.

The night was not as restful as the nights in Stroud Hospital had been. *Rustle rustle rustle . . . Snuffle.*

Snortle. Whimper . . . Scratch scratch scratch . . . Deep breath . . . Groan . . . Final Breath . . . Death Rattle . . . Long Silence . . . Rustle rustle rustle. And that was only Van Dyke. He was short of sleep, too. People had kept ringing him up in the middle of the night to ask if I'd had it yet. When Van Dyke gets overtired he talks in his sleep. And the really annoying thing about this is that he talks in Dutch.

'Ik geloof dat ik mijn enkel verstuikt heb!' he cried.

'What?' I asked. 'Who? Your uncle?'

'Sorry,' he muttered. (It's Sorry in Dutch, too.) Then there was a silence. I drifted back towards sleep.

'Het is te heet!' he exploded, throwing off the duvet.

'Stop it! And hush!' I whispered. 'You'll wake the baby.'

'Kunt u een kinderbedje in de kamer zetten?' And so on. No wonder he was so tired in the daytime. His sleeping life is packed with incident.

And Beano seems to have taken after him. Long before she could talk, even in these first few weeks of life, she was saying things in her sleep. 'Planets!' she would exclaim. 'Zithers!' 'Cowpox!' What with my family ranting away all night, the cats howling outside under the frozen yew tree, and the central heating growling and creaking to keep the arctic temperatures at bay, I was beginning to think that coming home was damned hard work.

Morning came. The baby was already awake, staring at the lining of her cot.

'Oh, God!' groaned Van Dyke. 'Ij have slept very badly. And I have had inkredibly tiring dreams.'

'Ah well,' I sighed sympathetically. 'Just muesli will do this morning, then. And a bit of toast, maybe. But wait! Can you just . . . change her nappy first?'

The peculiar thing was, I had completely lost my nerve. I did not trust myself to pick her up. If I hadn't been breast-feeding her, I'd have gone away and hid and left Van Dyke to do the lot. As it was, when she was sucking, I held her more and more awkwardly, looking down at her with increasing hysteria and panic. Was this right? Where was her other arm? Had it . . . dropped off in the night? Oh, there it was! I'd better move it . . . oh, no, it crunched! I must've hurt her! How terrible!

A day or so later, I was feeding her when she suddenly stopped, looked up at me, and vomited into the air with terrific force and accuracy – right into my face. I shrieked aloud in horror.

'Help! She's been sick! Hand me the book! I must look it up!'

'Ijs she all right?' Beano gave me a very beady look. She was instantly restored to tranquillity. She looked, today, rather like Edward G. Robinson.

Van Dyke carried her round the room telling her how beautiful she was and how splendidly she had been sick. I leafed urgently through the baby book.

'I knew it!' I cried. 'Projectile vomiting! Penelope Leach says that it's usually boys that get it but all the same . . . Oh, God! They have to have an operation!' I burst into tears. The thought of my tiny pixie-like child having to go back into hospital and face the surgeon's knife was unbearable.

The midwife came. She was, of course, Welsh, and of all midwives the most wonderful. She'd seen us through our antenatal breathings and her slow sing-song voice with its dying fall suggested somehow a safe haven: things being all right in the end. I was lying there counting the seconds until her arrival, the baby stretched out ghastly and grey on my knee, the milk curdled in my breasts, the blood seething in my wound, and at last she appeared: her beautiful face peeping round the door like an angel visiting a battlefield.

'Sorry to disturb you, Siieuw,' she sang in her quiet

way, and instantly the babe turned pink and waved her velvety paws about, and my knees stopped knocking and my milk and blood calmed down and the sun came out and a bird started singing and the amaryllis opened. So it was particularly frightening when she, of all people, said, after listening to the sick-saga, that there was a possibility – a very remote one – that it might be projectile vomiting and require a little operation. The doctor would visit and give her opinion.

'Till then, don't worry. It's probably just a bit of wind.' And she went. Yes, *went*! How could she do this to me?

Nightmare closed in behind her. I seized the phone. 'MUM!' I cried, and conveyed the awful tidings – with restraint and cheeriness, of course. 'Nothing to worry about,' I assured her. 'No, nothing to worry about!' echoed my mum – the *liar*. As soon as she'd put the phone down she ran and told my dad. My dad turned pale and took to his bed. My mother's knitting needles, which had been clicking away for months, seized up and rusted overnight. The piano went out of tune. The dog's fur fell out. All the dahlia tubers in the garage disintegrated. In the heart of the freezer, sixteen frozen eclairs sank silently into their paper cases. When the babe is ill, the world goes mad.

Chapter 16

She continued to be sick quite often: really sick, not just little possets of burped-up milk. Nice, harmless, white sick, of course. But plenty of it. The days were slightly lighter, but only literally. I lay in bed, feeding the baby and cringing back from her eruptions. Van Dyke cleaned up the sick, changed the nappies, answered the door, cooked the meals, did the washing up, answered the phone, reassured the parents, lied to the Bank Manager, fed the cat, opened the mail, washed the baby clothes, and then, after about six days, flung himself down on the bed and announced: 'Ij cannot go on!' Honestly, some people. No backbone.

'Have a rest,' I advised. 'I'll get you a cup of tea.' I hobbled down to those chilly, unfamiliar regions below stairs. I was feeling slightly stronger now. All the same, the kitchen seemed larger than I remembered. Was it really that far to the fridge? What a huge kettle! I could hardly lift it. It seemed like a giant's house. I felt like Alice, translated through the looking glass into a different dimension. Although looking glasses were things I kept well away from these days. I stared briefly through the kitchen window, though.

Good God! Some small yellow irises had come out, holding their gaudy heads clear of the carpet of snow. If only I had their guts. Or more to the point, if only I had their reproductive system.

Upstairs, Van Dyke was still lamenting. He couldn't go on, he said. We needed help. In Holland, after every confinement, the family is provided with full-time domestic help for a while. But then, Holland is light years ahead of the miserable UK when it comes to social organization. Even the prisons all have deep-pile carpets, videos, bidets and room service. I could see his point, though. He was supposed to be writing a piece of music, not carrying the cares of the world on his shoulders and trays of food up and down stairs all day. And though he had been a tower of strength so far, he had feet, if not of clay, then at least of feet. My mother was helping all she could: taking in our washing and delivering trifles on wheels three times a week. But what we needed was a full-time slave for a few days, to give Van Dyke a rest.

I rang my friend in the north. How far away, how blissfully unsuspecting their telephone bell sounded. How deeply unfair of me even to ask it of her. After all, she had her own small child, from whom she had never been separated even for one night. I'd have to be exceedingly casual and diplomatic: give her plenty of room to refuse. I'd drop the merest hint of domestic disorder only. Perhaps not even that. Perhaps nothing but a slight weariness at the edges of my voice, as I asked how they all were, up there. She answered the phone, at last.

'Help! Help!' I screeched. 'I can't stand it any more! We can't manage! Van Dyke has cracked up! And I'm worse than useless! For God's sake, come!' She came.

I later discovered that at the time of my phone call, Yorkshire was armpit-deep in snow, and that, in order to reach us, she'd had to harness up a team of huskies, navigate by the stars, and live off dried seal meat for days. Would she reach us in time? The miles melted away beneath her sinewy stride. Meanwhile, impossibly far south, the walls of our bedroom had shrunk to a few square feet of flapping canvas.

'Fear we cannot go on much longer,' I wrote in my milk-stained diary. 'Morale very low. Van Dyke talks of going down to the kitchen to get us a cup of cocoa but we all know in our hearts he will not make it. And even if he sets out, there is little prospect of his finding any cocoa there. Provisions are running out. We are all very depressed and gloomy, and this continuous sick strikes at the heart of our confidence. Van Dyke asked me yesterday to hand over the headache pills, and I obeyed. God knows what this means to a man of his self-esteem. We talk about rescue, but ...'

Even then we heard a sound. The sound of stout Yorkshire boots coming up our path. The doorbell rang – Van Dyke flew to answer it – a merry laugh was heard in the hall! Beano stopped crying and craned her ears in astonishment towards that brave new sound. Tyger is tall and glittering-eyed, with a lean and somewhat hungry look, but her merry laugh exploded like a sudden Christmas around our dank flagstones.

A tawny countenance appeared round the door. Tyger fixed her green eyes on the baby.

'Good morning, Miss Van Dyke,' she said, and lifted her out of her cot. 'Have you recently dined?'

'Ar,' affirmed Beano,

'And have you got a clean nappy on?'

'Haar.'

'Right then. Well take you for a walk around the house. Have they shown you the house, yet?'

'Nar.'

'Useless bastards. You come with me. I'll save you from them.' And she was gone. Van Dyke and I instantly went to sleep, in unison, the sick crusting gently on our sleeves.

It seemed like eight hours later, but was really only two, when Tyger returned, with Beano suspended across her chest in the babysling she herself had given us. She also carried other steaming delicacies on a tray. All the bits of old food which had been lying about in the corners of the fridge had been rescued, revived and meaning given to their exist-ence in a splendid creation known as Harrogate Hotpot. A bit like Lancashire Hotpot, only with more muck and brass. Bigod, it put new heart into us, and new muscle into t' mother's milk.

The next four days were extraordinary. Van Dyke actually managed to return to his composition. It was a piece for organ, called Jets d'Orgue. *Organ Jets* in English, I'm afraid. A decidedly projectile piece of music, really. I'm sure Beano's flamboyant arcs and parabolas must have been a great inspiration to him.

While Van Dyke composed, and I decomposed, Tyger went shopping, cooked heroic meals, cleaned the house, bought useful baby-equipment that we had not thought of, and carried Beano around in the sling. Once we recovered enough strength to peep outdoors, we bumped into Jack and Jill, our neigh-bours on the other side from Sidney Arbour. Jack and Jill had brought up two daughters, one of whom was now a mother herself, so they knew their onions.

'How's the baby?' inquired Jill. Once more an expression of Hamletian poignancy stole o'er my pallid profile.

'She seems to have ... projectile vomiting,' I sighed.

'Oh, that's good!' smiled Jill. 'You can point her at people you don't like.' Jill had spent some years in local politics. Perhaps that was what I needed.

I took courage from the fact that other people could joke about it. Surely they wouldn't joke about it if the

164

baby was going to die? I took courage also from Beano's surprising resilience. The days came and went, and she lived on.

All the same, her persistent vomiting didn't seem right. It was unnerving, in a way – a hint of her mortality, the thing I least wanted to confront. What's more, whenever it happened, I was faced with the fact that I had to make a whole new meal for her: that the milk I had produced was not strengthening my baby's bones, but making the carpet stink.

Another unfortunate irony was that nausea had always been my private phobia. I think this developed because I was never sick as a child. I was as reluctant with upward evacuations as with downward ones. Other children's vomitings deeply disgusted and terrified me. And then came university. Well, I don't suppose anyone could spend a term at Cambridge without vomiting heartily. For some, it may be the lingering apparatus of the class system that provokes a kind of social sickness: for some, the sheer indigestible acres of learning upon the shelves at the University Library. For me, it was the Newnham pork.

Permit me a brief visceral digression for a moment, and answer me this: what is it about institutional pork? Damned dangerous stuff, pig. Half the peoples of the world won't go near it, on principle, and I am now of their number. Pork. It even sounds horrible, like the sound made by someone choking to death on a piece of it. 'Pork! Pork! Aughk! PORK!' The Dutch for pig is Varken, which is even worse.

Anyway, the fateful occasion was a November evening in 1965. Or was it 1865? I was quite young then, so I think it must have been. The secret black and midnight hags who worked in the college kitchen were concocting the Servants' Revenge. Strike a blow against Pride and Privilege! Fell the Fellows and Undermine the Undergraduates! The secret weapon

165

was pork. The recipe must have been handed down for centuries in dripping dens in the fens:

> First, kill ye pigge, and see that it suffereth as much agonie as ye may endeavour to exact, so that ye torments of its brain doe seep into its glistening gristle and set forever there. Skin ye carcass and set it in a brackish pool till it stinketh. Encourage ye toads to crap thereon, the dish will gaine mightily thereby. Cut it into bittes and warme up ye ghastliest for a few seconds in a chafing dish, till it be scorched on the outward and still raw within . . .

Then, shortly after midnight . . . SLAM! Thud thud thud! All night I heard the thunder of girlish feet up and down in the corridor outside my room. I sat on the edge of my bed, shuddering but stubborn. I was never sick. Never. I stuffed my fingers in my ears to blot out the sounds of my fellow scholars' sufferings, and tried to tell my stomach to stop singing and dancing and turning somersaults and go back to being a boring old bag. I think I was the only girl in Newnham that night, who held out against the pork.

Next day, everyone else was pale but purged, but I kept to my room, green and poisoned. For a fortnight I sat on the edge of my bed with clenched teeth, shuddering. Then a friend brought me in a tray of cottage pie. That did the trick. I was out of the door, down fifty yards of corridor and head down in the loo before you could say Joan Robinson. On the way I almost ran over a startled girl called Barbara who later became a world-famous geographer, if there is such a thing. I sometimes wonder if her attraction towards remote and far-flung areas originated in that encounter in an English corridor: the walls, the awful nausea, the sense of no escape.

After the shock of that, of course, I copped a severe dose of nauseaphobia. People with nauseaphobia are never sick but always feel they're going to be. Formal situations brought it to fever pitch: a supervision, for example (what in Oxford they call a tutorial). Just you, your teacher, a roaring fire, a glass of sherry, and your essay. And, in my case, rising bile. Mrs Leavis was in the midst of the eighteenth-century poetry, but my fingernails were sinking deeper and deeper into her upholstery. Would she never pause for breath? Would I have time to make my excuses? Should I aim for the fireplace? Or would that be, as it were, *too* eighteenth century by far?

'What would you say was Robert Burns' unique contribution to the eighteenth-century lyric tradition?' she inquired, pausing for a moment, her bird-like head cocked sideways.

'I feel sick!' I roared, and ran for the door. Hidden in the cloakroom, of course, I did nothing but feel better. They sent me home in a taxi. (Queenie Leavis, incidentally, wrote a memorable comment at the foot of one of my most desperate-to-please essays. 'Cliché-ridden journalistic rubbish,' she scribbled. But I expect she was only being kind.)

A whole fleet of taxis ferried me away, in turn, from dinner parties, theatres, cinemas, lectures: the fresh air, the solitude and the privacy of the taxi instantly banishing all nausea and ushering in pink cheeks and the guilty desire for a cheese sandwich. I began to fear that I would never be able to participate in ordinary social life at all, but would be exiled to a windswept existence on some uninhabited promontory, where I would carve chessmen out of old walrus tusks and compose sad lyrics about my life of missed opportunities.

A few years later, when my migraines started to get more and more megaton, I was occasionally sick. Really sick. But only if the pain had become unendurable, and I'd got to the screaming-and-cursing-the-gods stage. So nausea remained, for me, something associated with extreme crisis: a feeling of being turned inside out, emptied and cancelled, a kind of rehearsal for death. This may account for the terror into which I was thrown by my baby's eruptions. Thanks, Fate. How accurately you fling your darts.

What was astonishing to me was that once it became clear that all this vomiting was simply the baby's immature digestion failing to organize its wind properly; once I realized that there wasn't any organic fault, no nasty hidden imperfection and therefore no need for the surgeon's knife, I adjusted to it all in no time. Ten years ago I'd have crossed the road to avoid a suspicious-looking puddle fifty yards ahead on the pavement, which would probably turn out to be no more than a dropped ice cream. Nowadays, I sit and eat a Chinese take-away amidst the debris of – but this subject has been explored beyond the hilt already. It is finished. You may unfasten your seat belts and smoke.

Chapter 17

As the days passed, there was a changing of the guard. At first, immediately after the birth, midwives come to visit you every day, but after about ten days the visits become less frequent and are performed by the Health Visitor. I was a bit offended when the Health Visitor first showed up. I'd got them confused with Health Inspectors – the people who go round poking their noses into unsavoury parts of restaurant kitchens to see if there is mouse in the moussaka or rat in the ratatouille. What a vile job! Thank God some brave souls are prepared to do it.

Being a Health Visitor can't be all that easy, either. It's their job to help and advise people who've just had babies – and God knows, if I'm typical, such people are badly in need of such help and advice. But there is something about a Health Visitor that brings out the beast in their clients. A midwife is so obviously a professional: those navy blue uniforms and the absurd little nurses' caps perched on their heads. Anyone wearing a hat that daft must know their stuff, for God's sake. But the unfortunate Health Visitors have to wear their own clothes: in other words, they're no better than you or me. Or are they, like plain clothes policemen, all the more sinister therefore?

Good Lord, you think, as the Health Visitor comes up the path, surely she's not visiting us! I mean, we're the middle class, for heaven's sake, we read the books: we can manage, can't we? Don't they trust us to feed and clothe our baby and watch over its tender sleep? Don't they understand that we anxious liberals will tear ourselves to bits in our attempts to do the right thing for the wretched child? Why aren't they off down the road watching over those baby-battering, drug-abusing, educationally subnormal parents in that other street? I mean, surely I'm doing it right, aren't I? Isn't it a waste of their time, visiting me? Or do they smell a rat?

Mine smelt a rat. Maybe she had been a Health Inspector in a previous incarnation. I was blithe at the time. We'd agreed the baby was just windy, that the sick was not sinister. I was positively relaxed. Oh dear, isn't it always the way? The light at the end of the tunnel is always an oncoming train. Yes, it would all clear up when she got a bit older and her digestive system matured. She squirmed about when examined, and waved her arms and legs about in what I took to be an extraordinarily accomplished way. She was, in fact, a perfect baby. Any fool could see that.

'I'll just weigh her,' said the Health Visitor, and got out her dinky little set of baby scales and plonked Beano upon them.

I hardly paid any attention to it. I knew she'd been a heavy baby at birth, but it was an irrelevance, surely. I wasn't interested in mere statistics. I think I even looked out of the window at the snow on the fir tree, and thought about something else.

'She's gained four ounces,' said the Health Visitor, with a curiously pursed-up expression of the lips, as she recorded it on her card. There was suddenly an odd atmosphere.

170

'Is that about normal?' I asked, in the first of a series of pathetically dumb remarks I was to make over the next few months.

'Well, I'd be happier if it was an ounce or two more.' There it is, my friends. An innocent enough little phrase. *I'd be happier if* . . . A tiny puncture is all you need, and your peace of mind is gone for ever. Well, for four or five months. And believe me, at the time, it seemed like for ever.

What are we women thinking of, anyway, meddling with scales and tables of averages? Who do we think we are – the Old Testament God? He who weighed everybody in the scales and then smited those that didn't quite measure up. What would the great Earth-Mother have to do with scales and with tables? With weighing, numbering and dividing? Wouldn't she have tucked the babe into her white breast, flung back her green hair and gone off to dance under the oaks?

Those who betray her, whose knees crumple at the verdict of the hateful scales, bring down on themselves their own punishment. Their hearts are shaken and their spirits broken by mere arithmetic. I know, my friends: alas, I am ashamed to say, it happened to me. I bowed beneath its fearful logic until my brows were black with mud and my breasts bitter with wormwood.

The trouble was I knew, secretly, that I was no good at it. Hadn't I completely lost my nerve at the start? Wasn't I still too nervous to bath her? As she fed, I was not relaxed. I did not croon lullabies and will my body to give her more. Instead, I urged myself not to give her too much in case she choked. I was tense with anxiety that she'd be sick, even after it was more or less agreed that there was nothing sinister about it, nothing organically wrong. So when the Health Visitor started to fret about the baby's weight gain, a massive cold whelm of feeling seemed

171

to rise up within me and I plunged into panic. *That's it*, I thought. *She's not going to grow. That's how bad a mother I am – I can't help her grow.*

She'd started off big, of course. That was the trouble. As a newborn she'd had great big dimpled arms and deeply upholstered legs. When you consider the mountains of food I'd gobbled up during my pregnancy, it wasn't really surprising. But in the weeks that followed, a more light and delicate creature began to emerge from the blubber. She was never thin, but she didn't pile on the flesh in the way that they seemed to expect. During the antenatal classes they'd said, 'We do hope you're going to breast-feed. Bottle-fed babies often put on too much weight.' I'd nodded virtuously.

And now here I was breast-feeding away and my baby wasn't putting on too much weight, and what were they saying? 'Give her a bottle,' suggested the Health Visitor after about two or three weeks. 'After her evening feed, when you've probably got least milk.'

'All right, yes, you're right, jolly good idea,' I heard someone say. I think it was someone pretending to be me. The real me had shrunk away inside myself and was hiding in my plantation of ribs. I could feel myself fluttering away in there, frightened, hurt and speechless. The impostor conducted the Health Visitor downstairs and saw her out.

'I really think spring's in the air today, don't you?' I heard her twitter, the inane other-me who had taken over my radio station. My press agent, my spokesman, the one who tells people what they want to hear, who agrees politely, who makes things easy for people. Despise her but she's useful. Without her, the real me would fly at them and peck their eyes out, and where would I be then? At the funnyfarm, probably.

I slunk off to the chemist's, feeling strangely

treacherous. I bought a bottle and some milk formula. Other women were doing the same, and they didn't look as I felt: weighed down with guilt and self-hatred. They had that 'just shopping' look. Would I ever be like them? I raced back to the car park where Van Dyke was nursing the screaming Beano. I leapt into the back seat, seized her, and gave her the breast. Instantly she closed her eyes and sucked blissfully. The world went dark, there was a flash of lightning, and hailstones as big as golf balls pelted the car. What on earth was going on?

That evening, after sterilizing the bottle and making up the formula – a procedure which seemed to take an hour and left the kitchen covered with fine white powder and smelling like a swimming pool – I gave Beano her evening suck, and then offered her the bottle. She spat it out with venomous disgust. I offered it again. She turned her head away. I followed her round with it, I coaxed the teat in between her reluctant lips, and then, inevitably – HUERLCH! She was sick. The milk I'd made myself, with my blood and my precious energy, was suddenly all over the floor.

This pattern went on for some weeks. We took the baby to the clinic, she was weighed and found wanting, the bottle was urged upon us as a good idea, we went home utterly demoralized and tried again, and Beano, astonished at our stupidity, spat it out. She sucked at my breast with every sign of contentment. She never rejected the breast or fussed at it or cried after a feed: she always slept. True, she cried for another feed again quite soon – about every two hours in the daytime, and every four at night. This meant I was unable to do anything much except lie around exhausted waiting for the next call. True, I felt dismal. But she seemed happy enough.

'Only two ounces this week,' announced the Health Visitor, looking rather severely at me over her

173

glasses. 'Very poor.' Very poor? Very poor? The real me was spinning out of control in a vortex of fear and uncertainty. Was I starving Beano? If so, why the hell wouldn't she drink from the bottle, the stupid baby? Why did she seem so contented?

'Oh dear. Well, all I can say is, we keep trying,' said the spokesman-me, apologetically, and went off for another week of furious feeding in pursuit of the average.

'Don't let them do this to you!' cried Tyger down the crackling telephone line. She was, alas, back in Yorkshire. 'It's just KXKSKing insane, this weighing business. Tell the stupid BSKSKSKers to XKAK off and just don't go to the XAXing Clinic any more.'

This advice filled me with relief. Of course! I could just not go. It hadn't occurred to me that I was a free agent, that attendance at the clinic was not compulsory, that I could just – oh, bliss! – *stay away*, that the dreaded Wednesday would not hang like a deadline over every week, that I could simply stay at home, throw the bottle away and play with Beano instead of peering anxiously at her wrists: *did they have a bracelet of fat around them or not?*

Van Dyke used to play with her a lot at nappy-changing when she'd coo and wave at him and kick her little legs about.

'Don't leave her bare like that for too long! I'd warn. 'Think of all the calories she's burning up, just trying to keep warm!' In my imagination I saw precious ounces of fat melting away for every second of naked acrobatics.

Imagine being in such a state, and then realizing that you could simply opt out. I would take Tyger's advice and stay away from the scales. Wednesday came, and I didn't go. With a delicious sense of guilt I had not felt since skiving off school to go brass-rubbing in Cirencester. (Nowadays they go glue-sniffing behind the VideoPorn Hire Centre – is it surprising we Wrinklies are nostalgic?) Wednesday was just Wednesday again. We went for a little drive to celebrate, and noticed primroses in the hedgerows. Was it really spring, out there? My heart gave a feeble attempt at a tiny skip.

Back home, though, there was a message waiting on the answering machine.

'Hello! This is the Health Visitor. We were sorry not to see you at Clinic today and we hope Beatrice is going on all right. Maybe you'd like to come down next week as the Doctor would like to see how she is.' I felt locked into my own personal winter again.

Next day, hey presto! The Health Visitor was there on the doorstep, all friendly and nice. She hoped we'd got the message? We'd got the message, all right. 'Hell's Visitors,' muttered Van Dyke.

As for Tyger's other piece of advice – to tell the stupid BSKSKSKers to XKAK off – well, this did not, somehow, seem appropriate. It didn't make it any easier that I liked the people concerned: they behaved throughout the whole charade in a gentle and considerate way, recording Beano's pathetic 3½ oz weight gains more in sorrow than anger. Once, when she gained 10 oz, they were jubilant. And when it all got too much for me one week and I burst into tears, the Health Visitor put her arm round me and said, 'You haven't failed, dear!' But the worship of the scales was absolute: its triumph over my willpower complete.

In the midst of this endless ordeal, this dark tunnel where I now lived, cut off from ordinary life, only dimly aware of the spring taking place as if it were on some remote planet; in the midst of it all, an extraordinary thing happened. I was feeding Beano one night, just before midnight, when she stopped, looked up at me, and suddenly broke into a delicious smile. 'Van Dyke!' I cried. 'She's smiling! Come quick! She's smiling at me!'

Van Dyke came, and to my amazement the baby turned her head to him and gave him a big smile, too. It was an extraordinary moment: something electric. It was as if somebody had just come into the room. Up till now, we'd admired her quiet alertness and her wakeful curiosity, but had received from her nothing but a rather stern stare. It was as if, all at once, she was a person at last: had joined us. This smile wreathed itself about my heart. It was the moment of a lifetime, never to be forgotten. I felt ravished by some divine spark of joy.

If the baby was starting to smile, surely things couldn't be that bad? All the same, the medical profession continued to fret over her steady average 3½ oz per week gain. Part of the trouble was that she did not like going to the clinic at all and started to misbehave dreadfully whenever we arrived in the car park. She was like a US draft dodger. As soon as she smelt the Health Centre she'd go limp and grey and glassy-eyed and loll about in my arms like a *Pietà*. The doctor, attempting to bounce her about on her knees, was not impressed.

'But surely,' Van Dyke was saying, 'even if she ijs not putting weight on fast enough, she's all right in other ways? She is so alert and active, there cannot be anything wrong.'

'I don't know,' the doctor shook her head. 'There are things – lots of little things that she should be doing, that she's not doing. Let's have another look at her next week.' Off we went again with our wretched, floppy failure of a baby. I felt deadened by failure in an area that was beyond my control.

It was an odd feeling. For all of my life up till now, I'd rushed off to the doctor every fortnight or so with some imaginary ailment. 'It's my hands!' I'd cry. 'They've gone mottled! Do you think it's serious?' 'It's my neck! Something went twang the other day and now I can't even turn my head.' 'It's my kidneys! I peed ten times yesterday – that can't be normal, can it?'

And all the time the doctors reassured me. *You have the healthiest kidneys in Hampstead*, they said at the Royal Northern Hospital, though, come to think of it, that's not saying much. *It's all perfectly normal. People's hands just go mottled sometimes. It's nothing to worry about.*

Nothing to worry about had been their message up till now, when I'd been sure I was dying. Now with Beano there were no unnerving symptoms I could see at all, and the message was, *Wait a minute, now! You really have got something to worry about, here.* It was the world turned upside down.

'Ring your local National Childbirth Trust Breast-feeding Counsellor,' ordered Tyger.

'My what?' But yes, I did have her number. It had been given to me by the angelic midwife all those weeks ago when Beano was ten days old and I didn't have a care in the world apart from being half dead. Ah, the Golden Age! I rang the number and told my tale.

'I think you're doing brilliantly!' she shrieked. They all say that, incidentally. During the Battle of the Breasts I consulted several breast-feeding counsellors and they all said I was doing brilliantly. 'I think they'd say you were doing brilliantly –' if the baby was stuck up the chimney and your tits were caught in the mangle. All the same, it cheered me up a bit. She recommended a book and lent me a breast pump.

So every day after the feed I pumped out my breasts in time with the Scarlatti on the radio (dreading the fast movement). I stared out of the window and noticed that leaves were bursting from every plant. This time two years ago I'd been spending eight hours a day in the garden. But at the moment nothing seemed more remote than the prospect of gardening except, perhaps, going to see the latest Woody Allen film and having a meal in Soho afterwards, or cycling through a city park, or idling around an art gallery.

So why didn't I feel resentful, sitting here day after day, pumping away . . . 2 oz, 3 oz . . . milk which the baby would probably reject when offered to her in a bottle as extra pudding after her feed? I suppose the answer was, I had discovered true love. The love which repays slavery and exhaustion with a brief smile. But what a smile! It was more than enough. My present prostration was somehow sweeter than all the pleasures of my past life.

Chapter 18

The month of May brought with it a strange and exotic promise: that of a holiday, booked way back in January, before Beano's birth. We'd rented a house in the Lake District to share with Tyger and her family, and a friend called Matthew, an unconfirmed bachelor.

'Surely by the end of May the weather will have got a bit spring-like even up in the Lake District,' I'd speculated.

'Maybe. But what about you? Are you sure you'll feel up to it? Won't you feel absolutely XKAKed?' asked Tyger.

'Oh, I don't know. She'll be three months old by then. I mean, three months! Surely we'll be more or less back to normal?' There was a hesitation for a moment: all I could hear was the wind wuthering up and down outside Tyger's back door.

'Well, if you're BSKSKZ it'll be all right . . .'

'Oh go on! Go ahead and book it! We'll manage somehow. We'll be there – by hook or by crook.'

Tyger booked it, but of course, when the time came, not only was the weather almost as bad as it had been in January, but Van Dyke and I were still candidates for the Special Care Unit ourselves.

Most nights we went to bed ten minutes after the baby had gone to sleep. We couldn't even summon up the energy necessary to slump in front of the TV. How in the world were we going to manage to pack up all the baby's kingdom, drive hundreds of miles north, keep her well and happy and notice the odd mountain, without losing consciousness? Let alone climb Great Gable or go snorkelling in Wastwater.

All the same, we had to try. Apart from anything else, we had to go to Holland in midsummer, so we might as well get some travel practice in. After all, if you levelled all the mountains, drained all the lakes into dykes, and built greenhouses over seventy-five per cent of the land, the Lake District would be quite like Holland. It's hard to imagine William Wordsworth striding manfully over the polder, but all the same, there is the rain. Mind you, anywhere else in Britain would've been the same that summer, when it came to rain. Which it usually did.

Just the thought of this holiday was enough to give me quite a bad migraine the day before we were due to leave. Migraines are my body's way of saying Forget It. But on the appointed day, there we were driving up the motorway, with Beano tucked up in her carrycot on the back seat and all her gear packed away in the boot. She was, I reflected, a bit like a circus with her travelcot and her changing mat and her bouncing chair and her things on strings. At least we didn't have to pack any food for her.

At this stage, of course, all her food was still in my contemptible old breasts, but we did take the bottle and a packet of Osterfeed 'just in case'. Just in case what, I'm not exactly sure, but it had to do, I believe, with the chances of my personal extinction, which seemed, on that day, particularly high. I had to wear three pairs of sunglasses at once just to keep my eyes open – and this was travelling north on a dark and rainy day. Still, there was a bright side to it all: we were going to have to miss at least two clinics.

The journey was made infinitely more comfortable, however, by the fact that the rusting Ford Escort had given way to a sleek black Rover. I felt a bit like the Chief Constable of Yorkshire as we glided through Bingley and Keighley, except that I was breast-feeding in the back. We had got to the point, with the old car, that the doors virtually had to be held on, and I had begun to feel that a babe as sacred as ours should have something a little more substantial between it and the juggernauts.

The Rover was a used car, and because no one in Gloucestershire would be so stupid as to buy a car much too wide to squeeze through the narrow lanes, and much too greedy, petrologically speaking, for one to hold one's head up at Green Festivals, it was fairly cheap. So we bought it. I knew it was the next best thing to a tank. And as we negotiated the rock-strewn tracks of the North Country, I felt we'd been justified. I'm sure the rusting old Escort would've split open on a chunk of granite, and the baby been stolen by kestrels.

The hired house looked over a minor lake – Esthshthwaite, I think it was called – and was disturbingly immaculate; but within thirty minutes of our arrival, the flawless green carpet in the sitting-room was covered with babysick and the bathroom windowsill covered with *Star Wars* figurines belonging to Tyger's cub. Not that he is an orthodox little boy. He spends much of his time making lavender bags and plum puddings.

Tyger took Beano for a walk while we unpacked. She popped the enchanted baby into the sling and disappeared over the wall.

'Where have your useless parents hidden the Osterfeed?' I heard her ask Beano as they went. 'Shall I throw it in the lake?' Beyond the garden, which was pleasant, rugged and well planted, was a forest and stream. Or so they told me. Just walking round the garden was exertion for me. I spent a lot of time sitting in an armchair and staring out at the view, like a Cumberland Octogenarian waiting for William Wordsworth to immortalize me before the Grim Reaper came creeping up through the rocks and ferns and grabbed me by the scruff of the soul.

He had been to school in the neighbouring town (Wordsworth, not the Grim Reaper. How do you tell the difference? Well, I've heard that the Grim Reaper is a lot more fun). Hawkshead was its name, and judging by the surviving portraits of Wordsworth it might justifiably also have been applied to himself. My chief memories of this holiday revolve around Hawkshead. I was just about strong enough to be driven there (a five-minute experience) and then to walk about there (a ten-minute experience, and mercifully level).

It was a very charming place. The tiny square was closed to traffic, all the houses were whitewashed, and we loitered in alleyways and discovered tiny gardens poised above secret streams. This, as far as I was concerned, was the acceptable face of the Lake District. A convivial and intimate settlement, in my mind, is worth a hundred beetling crags.

Back at the ranch, I slept some excellent sleeps. This holiday, I realized, chiefly meant to me a different view from the bedroom window. But I wasn't entirely idle: there was the walk, for example, from my bed to my favourite armchair. There was also armchair travel. I dipped into several guides to the lakes. But my chief reading matter was an Italian guidebook to the village of San Gimignano, which I'd visited in 1969.

Some freakish impulse had led me to pack it, in case the Lake District proved too frighteningly north-ern – which it did. A curiously Victorian melan-

182

choly air seems to hang over the Lake District. Even the rain sometimes seems nineteenth century: inexorable and unrepentant. At such times I plunged into my Guide Book to San Gimignano, and was instantly transported to Tuscany.

Not far from this church there is the Etruscan Cemetery where many interesting tombs have been excavated . . .

Tyger burst in, raindrops glinting in her eyebrows, and fresh trout twitching in her plastic bag.

'We've just been to Coniston!' she announced. 'It rained. We went on the lake. Then it snowed.'

'What was it like?'

'Rather good. But we couldn't see the mountains because of the fog.' Tyger is more what you'd call a northern spirit. One of the Northern lights. But back to San Gimignano.

Outside San Matteo Gate, after one kilometre, there is a crossroad, taking the dusty road on the left one meets the formerly Convent of Cappuccini.

Ah, the dusty road! I shifted Beano on to the other breast. A handful of hailstones hit the window.

Here we can admire a wonderful painting by Benozzo Gozzoli. It is showing St Sebastian while he is opening his cloak to protect the people from the pest in 1464.

That's his story, anyway.

'Ij will make a chicken risotto for supper!' volunteered Van Dyke. Tyger retired to the bath with her cub. Lamb read a guidebook to the Lake District and mildly picked his nose. Beano fell asleep in the crook of my arm. A gale shook the thorn bushes outside. But I was deep in Renaissance art.

Madonna with Child by Pier Francesco Fiorentino
. . . Madonna with Child by Benozzo Gozzoli . . . ,

and I'm not one to gossip, but

Madonna with Child by unknown Sienese of the
13th century.

What about the frescoes in the Church of Sant'Agostino? What glimpses will they give us into the private lives of the saints?

12. *Here are some scenes representing the Hermits*
    of Mount Pisan.
13. *Monica's death.*

Monica? Who was she? Ah, an earlier fresco gives us a clue, viz:

3. *S. Monica praying for his son Agostino and*
   blesses him.

With a dad called Monica, is it surprising Agostino took to the church? The devil may have the best tunes but the Church certainly has the best frocks. And what a triumphant end was in store!

15. *St Augustine triumphs over the heretic Fortune.*
16. *St Augustine in hestacy* (sic).

Monica would've been proud.
    'Shall we go to Wastwater tomorrow, I wonder?' murmured Lamb, from the depths of the other guidebook. 'It says here it's the grimmest and most forbidding part of the Lake District.'
    But I was in the Museum of San Gimignano.

*He who lingers in the rooms of our museum lives
again at the time of those past ages. Those small
things well shaped, those home-tods, those arms
corroded by time, the collection of coats of arm, the
stone graves, the urnes and the Etruscan things with
the same roon where all this is gathered can speak
to the mind and heart with an advising speaking apt
to remind the past generations who left such an
indelible trace of greatness, kindness and strength.*

Next day we went to Ruskin's house, Brantwood,
overlooking Coniston. I walked in the garden for ten
minutes, looked at the drawings for two minutes, and
spent two and a half hours having tea and cakes.
Ruskin, I recalled, had been born on the same day as
my baby, and was also the child of elderly parents. He
had lost his heart to Renaissance Italy, and finding
himself in a state of great antiquity in the Lake
District many decades later, had consented to be
propped against a wall to have his photograph taken.
He had also been mad about little girls. My heart
warmed to him.

Chapter 19

I had come north to contemplate the mountains, and ended up smiling at the shade of Ruskin. But then, it wasn't quite the holiday I'd been expecting. Wind whirled about the garden, dashing the still bare twigs into shattered fragments. It was just possible to sit out, or rather, to lie, if you wrapped yourself in an Arctic sleeping bag and prostrated yourself behind the rockery. This is not the ideal posture or setting from which to enjoy a garden party, however, especially since the north wind does tend to whip one's words, not to mention one's cucumber sandwiches, over the horizon towards Great Gable.

So we retired indoors. It was a pity the house was so modern. With the wind shrieking in the chimney, it would've been cosy to lie on a bearskin by a crackling log fire, the soft glow of candlelight making us all look seventeen again, while Tyger or Lamb (both excellent cooks) whipped up an authentic Cumbrian plum crumble. However, we endured the electricity and other mod cons with heroic resignation. At least it made the cooking easier.

And the meals were one of the highlights of the holiday, especially as I was excused cooking duties owing to being a nursing mother, and therefore, as it were, already involved rather intimately in the catering business. Otherwise, they took it in turns, starting with Matthew the Bachelor. Bachelor cuisine, in my experience, can defy all the culinary traditions and yet prove surprisingly tasty. The Young Journalist of the Year, for example, who had shared my London house, regularly stirred cheese and oregano into his porridge and was once observed sprinkling Coca-Cola over his salad.

But Matthew's skill was more orthodox, and inclined to the Mediterranean. He was famous for his salad dressing, which combined olive oil, lemon juice, garlic, and several bits of aromatic old southern herb in such perfect harmony that in the past I had been tempted to propose marriage to him on the spot. He would've refused though.

Salad dressing on its own, however, isn't all that filling, so we were relieved when he returned from Hawkshead with a dead bird – possibly a hawk – and put it in the oven. It proved to be a chicken, but of course up there in the Lake District chickens are all lean and brown and sinewy. It comes from all that wandering over the fells. (See Wordsworth's poem, *The Blasted Hen*.) When finally roast bird and exquisite salad were set before us, the wind and weather paled into insignificance before the reliable thrills of sheer greed.

Next day it was Van Dyke's turn to cook. I had brought my World Cookery book, so the gourmet dishes of the entire planet were at our disposal. Would Van Dyke regale us with *Boerwors*, *Monkey Gland Steak* or *Koeksisters* (all Boer delicacies – if that's not a contradiction in terms). Or would he go all South American and provide *Puchero*, *Cuchuco*, and *Caldo da Quimgombo*? If he could get the ingredients, that is. I'm not sure what the Hawkshead grocer would've made of a request for quails or vine leaves, let alone *gombo*.

But the Dutch are nothing if not economical, and Van Dyke conjured up a chicken risotto with the remains of the previous night's roast. This pattern of good husbandry was continued the following night by Tyger. (It had been Men First, to show how emancipated we were.) Tyger found a mound of rice left over from the previous day and adroitly transformed it into a rice pudding.

Lamb picked at it delicately with his spoon. 'How curious,' he observed. 'There appears to be a piece of chicken in this rice pudding.' Yes. It had been no mere mound of rice. It had been the remains of Van Dyke's chicken risotto. I don't know why the presence of bits of chicken in the rice pudding was so disturbing. It was as if we had transgressed an important Old Testament law, and forked lightning would flash down on Esthwaite for our transgression.

Well, forked lightning more or less did flash down, so we abandoned plans for an evening stroll and instead set about getting drunk and playing charades. The common or garden charades about titles of books, films, plays, etc, were soon exhausted. (But not before Lamb had almost given himself a hernia trying to convey the whole concept of *Gone With The Wind*.) We then went on to the hard stuff: charades of the names of Tube stations.

Tufnell Park was seized on by Tyger. Her portrayal of Tough Nell conjured up rather terrifying images of a women's vigilante group. Then it was Van Dyke's turn. He could only remember the name of one Tube station, King's Cross, and gave a rather sheepish performance of an enraged monarch. It's not the Dutch's strong point, royalty. Their royal family could be just anybody. I bet they even go to the launderette.

Matthew came next, and transfixed us with his embodiment of Marble Arch: the whole concept. In fact, the creative genius of this performance swept us on into another game altogether: Ancient Monuments. So as the midnight hour approached, when any sane person would begin to think of cocoa and bed, we beheld the wonders of the world.

Matthew as the Colossus of Rhodes was pretty good, especially as he's not an inch over 5 feet 7 inches, and Lamb's Leaning Tower of Pisa inspired Van Dyke to an epic attempt to convey the entire city of Venice sinking into the lagoon. My own modest contribution, assisted by Van Dyke's car torch, was the Cerne Abbas Giant, and it was at this moment that Tyger, dozing on the sofa, was mistaken for the Sphinx. (Not, I might add, for the first time in her life.)

Clouds scudded across the moon, the shade of William Wordsworth slid across the silvery surface of Esthwaite, but we were all oblivious: pushing forward the frontiers of silly games. We had now gone beyond Ancient Monuments and were engrossed in the adverb game. The idea is that you come into the room in the manner of an adverb, and people ask you to do things which you perform in the same manner. (e.g., if the adverb was *appallingly*, you'd probably never manage to get through the door at all, catching your ankle on the lintel and getting your nose stuck in the keyhole).

After the adverb game came the Coming-Into-The-Room-In-The-Manner-Of-A-Famous-Person game. Van Dyke recognized Matthew's Coming-Into-The-Room-As-President-Reagan before the door was even open properly: it was the ostentatiously modest-but-manly way the doorknob twitched. Tyger, when her turn came, kept falling over, sighing, and saying, 'Oh, God! Oh, God!'

This mystified us for a long time and for a moment I wondered if she'd forgotten we were doing famous people and was back on monuments. The Campanile of St Mark's, Venice, apparently, collapsed with just such immense dignity a few hundred years ago, accompanied, the chroniclers assure us, with a melancholy sign. But no! 'Twas not the Campanile she was impersonating, 'twas my babe. Tyger's view of Beano as world-weary made me slightly uneasy. I did hope the poor creature would grow up to enjoy life a bit, at least.

There was always food. Hey, yes! My companions were all stretched forth, inert, upon horizontal surfaces, but I was experiencing a queer burst of energy.

'I know!' I cried. 'Let's do Great Dishes of World Cookery!' Tyger refused to get up, but offered to lie on the sofa in the manner of an exotic soup. I suggested *Caldo da Quimgombo* but she gave me a dismissive glare and merely writhed her fingers about in a faintly octopussy way. It turned out to be *Bouillabaisse*, of course.

Van Dyke came into the room in the manner of minced meat balls, apparently a Dutch treat but a highly painful charade. Lamb personified (there was no need for him to act) orange meringue pie, and though I say so myself, I think I gave a spirited account of Cock-a-Leekie soup.

But it was Matthew who performed the *coup de grâce* to the evening's entertainment. It had been his intention to convey the essence of *Champignons à la Grecque*. We'd got as far as *Champignons à la*, and Matthew was attempting to perform a Zorba-like Greek dance, when the late hour, the fatigue, the great indulgence in food and wine all conspired to undermine his self-control and he broke wind with some violence in mid-caper and dived, mortified with shame, behind the sofa.

'*Champignons à la Death by Farting!*' cried Tyger, and you know, the odd thing was, I'm sure that's exactly what caused my trouble in Crete back in 1967.

And so to bed. Beano was snortling gently in her

carrycot: the moon was high, the night was mild. But pleasure must be paid for, and I wasn't entirely surprised at about 5 a.m. to discover that I had a raging migraine. I hadn't drunk anything much by the standards of real people, but even a thimbleful of Muscadet, combined with prolonged mucking-about long past bedtime, can have fatal results.

Fellow migrane-sufferers will know the feeling of having an iron stake driven through your eyeball and into your brain, nailing you to the pillow: the raging thirst, the quivering nausea, the hot and cold shudders, the hatred of light. Merely drawing the curtains was not enough: I beseeched Van Dyke to cover the window with a thick blanket as well, if not the carpet off the floor.

Beano was brought in from time to time and laid at my breast. It seemed to be business as usual at the restaurant. She stared at me rather incredulously, her dark eyes gleaming in the black cavern of bedclothes. I expect she thought I was playing some kind of game. Another charade, perhaps. The Dark Ages; whole concept.

'Please don't let her inherit this,' I croaked feverishly to whatever gods were listening. 'Never, never, no no no!' Migraines increase one's self-pity to boiling point, and encourage moans, curses and emotional declarations of passion. Every migraine is like a deathbed. You seize the sleeve of a passing kinsman and winge, 'I'm sorry I've been such a swine to you! I've always loved you really!'

Once the rage, the tears, and the screams of despair have all been rehearsed, the best thing is to lie very still and think of something pleasant. It takes hours and hours for the torment to run its course, so you might as well try and detach yourself from the pain by insisting, albeit gently, on pleasure.

My mind was suddenly flooded with images of my London garden. It was over a year now since I'd left it.

A whole summer had gone by, during which it had opened and bloomed for other eyes, and though I didn't begrudge its new owners one iota of delight, I did miss it dreadfully. There had been no garden last summer in Wales, and when we'd moved to Stroud we'd been too busy working on the house to spend any time in the garden at all.

And now this new, rain-soaked summer was unfolding, and I was so utterly exhausted and spent that it was quite clear that I wouldn't be able to do anything for the new Stroud garden when I got home. It would gradually revert to a grassy bank; weeds would choke its once-handsome border; ruin and desolation would take over. And I knew I wouldn't really feel at home until I'd managed to go out and get to know this new garden by caring for it and changing it; making clear to it that I cared for it and would do my bit if it did its bit. Gardening is the most passionate of love affairs and when it's not working, it feels terrible, like love gone wrong. Fellow gardeners will understand.

And fellow migraine-suffering gardeners will not be surprised, therefore, to learn that I lay there in the dark with the odd tear trickling down my cheek, going for a walk, in my mind, through my old London garden in midsummer.

I opened the back door. (What a shoddy piece of work that back door was! I should never have employed those Turkish builders, great though my admiration is for the Ottoman Empire. They stood around all day while walls collapsed around them and fountains burst from damaged piping and all they could say was things that sounded like, 'Sushitzon boiling-bulldogz.' If I'd been able to communicate with them I might have ended up with a halfway decent back door, made out of something at least halfway wood, instead of what I'd ended up with: one of reinforced cardboard with a nasty aluminium handle that looked like a bird of prey's head.)

But never mind! The despised door opened and I stepped out into the whitewashed backyard. Here were my troughs of shade-loving plants: white begonias and nicotianas and busy lizzies, all rather tender and soft in pink and white, the nicotianas imparting a heady scent on velvety nights. And then, the ginger cat at my heels, I passed the tropical bulk of my castor oil plant, waving its leaves at me like big green hands.

Here was my elder bush, which had sprung up of its own accord and kept the witches away, and now a tiny curving path led off between the stars of magnolia and the palmy fronds of sumach on the left, and the gold sprays of forsythia and white foam of morello cherry blossom on the right. (The advantage of the mental excursion is that you have everything blooming at once.)

Here was a small circular lawn, ringed with bamboo, lilies, and the grey mist of artemesia, and, further back, the white and green explosion of *Cornus alba elegantissima* with its wild red stems upflung in winter, but now hidden in its own leaf and by the mounds of potentilla in front of it, dotted with simple stars. On my left, the white spires of Canterbury Bells and, in between the cracks in the paving, a minute viola. This plant had been gathered by my godmother's friend's mother on honeymoon in Whitby around 1900, and my present little freckled specimens had all descended from this happy souvenir.

Under an arch, now, heavy with the white rose Iceberg, given to me by tiny Alice, and intertwined with the Iceberg a purple clematis, the only plant I'd brought with me from Cambridge years and years ago. And we are in the vegetable garden. Rows of tomato plants spreading gently in the heat, their leaves giving off a delicious sharp green smell when

193

touched. And opposite them my strawberry plants, which sneaked through the chainlink fencing to delight the Jewish children next door.

Rows of peas and beans, without which no summer is a summer, with the scarlet runners scrambling up their bamboo poles, and then my greenhouse. I grew 4,000 seedlings in there once. Or was it 2,000? It felt like four, anyway. My back nearly broke from hours and hours of pricking out.

Inside the air is always still and the sun hot, and my melon plants were sprawling on their shelf. The first year I managed two the size of golf balls, the second year four the size of cricket balls – but they split because I watered them at the wrong moment. That's what I love about gardening: you have to be patient. One lifetime's not nearly enough. The melon's delicious scent fills the stillness, encouraging the cucumbers towards sweetness.

Back outside, and down the last bit of garden – a sort of wild lawn with a little terrace at the bottom, against a sunny wall. Here is my fig tree with its friend the rue at its feet: my vines, my honeysuckles, and next door's hops romping along the fence: a green screen. Here I crash down, like Andrew Marvell, into the deep grass, to look up through the patchwork of fig leaves through the blue air, to heaven's very floor.

Beyond the blue was the blackness. A door opened in the blackness. Someone was joining me.

'Hello, Sue,' whispered Van Dyke. 'Are jou awake?' I stirred in my swamp of bedclothes.

'Nar nar nar!' said a husky little voice in my ear, and Beano cuddled up to me in the bed.

'We hav just made a fantastiek walk,' said Van Dyke. 'Just Beano and me. I put her in the sling and we walked up through the forest and it had been raining and everywhere it smelt of rain and the wet trees. And then a blackbird suddenly started singing: it was just before the sun went down and it was singing, really. And Beano was listening to it. You could see by her eyes she was trying to see where the sound was coming from. It was fantastiek. I was nearly crying, really ... How are you feeling now, darling?'

I thought I was feeling a lot better.

Chapter 20

When we got home, the first thing on the agenda was Help. What they used to call Service. Help implies that the good souls who come to your house to scrape the dreadful gunge off the cooker are working shoulder-to-shoulder with you out of the goodness of their hearts. Service implies that the people who perform these tasks are somehow destined, as a class, to do so, and that they ought to feel deeply honoured to spend their days scraping up your crud while you sip Pimm's out on the terrace and watch the sun set on the Empire. I advertised for a cleaner.

'You've advertised for a cleaner?' gasped one of my childless London friends. She was appalled. 'Do you mean you expect *other people* to clean up your mess?'

'Well, it's a job, isn't it?' I faltered. 'Look at it this way. I'm creating employment. And look at it another way – if I don't get somebody, I shall never manage to get any work done at all, and then we shall have to sell the house.'

She was silent at the prospect of such a chaotic life style, precariously balanced on the edge of overdraft and of domestic disorder. If we'd been sensible, and thought about it rationally, Van Dyke and I should never have had a child. Thank goodness we had rushed into it instead, borne along by half-baked romanticism and irresistible instinct. When pregnant I had wondered what it would be like to have a baby, and had imagined myself writing with the babe asleep in a basket under my table. But the fact was—

'She has not come into the world to sleep,' observed Van Dyke. Indeed, Beano spent most of the daytime hours awake. Since she was still too young to sit up and play, we had to carry her about and show her new things all the time. Socially, she was more exhausting than the most crowded of drinks-parties. It wasn't that she was demanding, exactly. She didn't shriek for attention. But the intensity of her gaze provoked a reciprocal intensity in us.

'Look, here we are in the garden,' I'd whisper into one of her large pointy ears. 'My God! Look how tall these weeds are! I must get a gardener. This is a laurel bush. And this is a yew tree, my darling. And this is a laburnum.'

'Haaaaaar!'

'Yes, you can touch, but don't EAT IT! It's poisonous. They're all poisonous. Sometimes I think every plant in this goddam garden is poisonous. Not nice! Ugh! NASTY! Bad pain in the tummy. Now, this is holly.'

'Hooooo!'

'Yes, holly. Also poisonous, and – GENTLY! Don't squeeze it! You'll – I told you so. Prickly! Yes! Hurts. Only a bit, though. Don't be such a baby. Although, I suppose you are a baby, aren't you? So why shouldn't you *be such a baby* while the going's good? Oh, no, it's started to rain again. So we must go in again. Go in.'

'Maio Laio.'

'Mummy and Beano go in again. Hell! I've trodden on a slug. Ugh! How disgusting! At least, I find them disgusting. You are free to disagree, of course. But please don't find them delicious. So, my darling, that

197

was the garden. Lovely, wasn't it? Do you see why Mummy loves the garden so much? Apart from the poisonous plants and the prickly plants and the slimy slugs and the rain, it's wonderful, isn't it?'

'Naaaaaar.'

'My God, I'm tired out. I must have a cup of tea. There, sit in your high chair for a moment. You're so heavy. Well, by my standards, at least. There you are! Where are the damned straps? Sit still for a minute, while Mummy looks for the – DON'T TOUCH THAT! Nasty! Electricity! Poisonous and prickly, my darling, beyond imagination! Oh God, I can't bear the thought of it! Come here and give me a hug! And promise never to touch that plug again!'

'Hoh! Hoh!'

'Yes, I know, I put your high chair by the socket. All Mummy's fault. Mummy a complete berk. Mummy exhausted. Only another half hour and then Daddy's turn. Why don't we go upstairs and just sit on the sofa? Sod the tea. Nice on the sofa. Horizontal. Let go of my hair, there's a darling, damn you. You're supposed to be a weak, underfed and floppy baby: how can you be so sodding strong?'

In the end I would lapse into silence, which Beano enjoyed, of course, much more. She was a saturnine soul. 'The most world-weary baby I've ever seen,' observed Tyger. Her smiles were not ready and gregarious. 'Slow to come, and crystalline,' remarked a friend who had been working away for one for three minutes.

Since there seemed little prospect of her sleeping while we worked, we started taking it in turns to look after her while the other attempted to work. Of course, I was so exhausted by these intense monologues, and with my attempts to wring a smile from her inscrutable features, that when at last Van Dyke took over I fled not to my desk but to my bed.

Down in the kitchen, the dirty dishes were the

first inanimate objects to work out a reproduction method. Soon there were whole families of cups, half-filled with cold tea, in every room in the house. Under our bed the socks preferred to dissolve their marriages and set up a singles bar. The mists of time settled triumphantly on the mirrors, which was a relief. It would be a long time before I ever looked in a mirror with much more than resignation. Perhaps never. I had regained a figure after Beano's birth, but it was somebody else's.

Apart from baby-fatigue, domestic disorder, and personal dereliction, there was the serious business of work to consider. Transworld Publishers had recently signed me up on a contract. I forget the exact details but I think they'd offered me two pounds to write a few thousand books before March. I was aware that up in my study there were lots of pieces of paper which had not been written upon. What's more, if I didn't do something about it soon, I knew that things would fly apart, the centre would not hold, and mere anarchy would be loosed upon our bank account. It would be a shame to have to sell the house so soon after buying it, especially since we were clearly not in a condition to organize the removal of six dirty mugs downstairs, let alone a houseful of personal effects into a muddy caravan or desirable garage.

I trust I have set forth compelling reasons why domestic help was now a necessity. I rest my case, M'Lud. Although I admire the moral absolutism of my childless friend in London who would never dream of asking anyone else to clear up her mess, I had to conclude that moral absolutism was a luxury I could no longer afford. We would start with a cleaner, move on swiftly to a part-time nanny and occasional gardener, and then, once I got a taste for it, engage a Malayan masseur and a Caribbean chauffeur with white suit and peaked cap.

Mrs Heaven was the first to answer the advertisement. She rang up one morning and I foolishly heard myself asking her round for an interview in half an hour. Van Dyke came in to find me thrusting old newspapers under the sofa and moving dirty cups behind the curtains.

'Mrs Heaven is coming at ten for an interview!' I cried. 'Do you mind moving those bags of garbage out of the hall? I can smell the disposable nappies from here!'

'But why clean up when you're interviewing a cleaner?' asked Van Dyke. 'Surely it ijs better to let her see the real state of thijngs?'

'I don't know. If she sees how filthy everywhere is, she might think—'

'Ja, but—' This promising exchange of views was interrupted by the doorbell.

'Go and get us all a cup of coffee,' I hissed. 'I'll take her into the sitting-room.' I opened the door and Mrs Heaven fell on me.

'Hello dear is this the right place I nearly went next door got a mind like a sieve is this the baby hello love she's a little lovey ent she got five boys meself.'

'Hello! Come in!' I managed to squeak, though it is quite hard to speak at all when your nostrils are firmly closed, as mine were, against the overpowering stench emanating from Mrs Heaven's person.

She was fortyish, gypsyish, and dressed in the fashions of the mid-Sixties: tall clumpy boots, now very down at heel; short skirt, now irretrievably rucked up; and long straight hair that gleamed with grease. Had she, I wondered, recently had a bath? And when I say recently, I mean within the past month. I guessed not. She was, if anyone ever was, High Heaven.

'Nice room you got here we got a coal fire too, 'ave to be careful with the kiddies though one o'mine got a terrible burn all up 'is arm and Gary that's my eldest

200

tipped the kettle over hisself when we was three. Nice candlesticks you got there real silver ent they I bet they're worth a bob or two.'

Despairingly I thought of Van Dyke making the cup of coffee in the kitchen. He was the very worst person to be doing it. Because he uses hot milk. And you can imagine what that meant: ten more minutes of High Heaven while she waited for her coffee to cool.

Why go on with this charade? Why had I ever said, *Hello, come in,* when anyone with a grain of sense of smell would have said *Goodbye, stay out.* I buried my nose in my baby's skull and tried to lose myself in the sweet scent of strawberries which always hangs about there.

'Gorgeous ent she?' cried Mrs Heaven and suddenly snatched the babe in a deft gypsyish swoop. 'Gorgeous ent you you little beauty.' She bounced Beano vigorously on her bare, brown, bony knees.

Be sick now, Beano, I pleaded silently. *If you love your mummy, old girl, be sick now.* But Beano wasn't being sick quite so often, these days.

'Got five boys meself always wanted a girl ent she sweet ent you pretty little chicky then ducks. I'll steal yer I'll steal yer away. You want to come 'ome with Brenda, eh?' Beano's face creased in alarm.

'Waaaaaaar! Laaaaaaar!'

'She's hungry,' I faltered, making a feeble gesture towards her. 'Maybe I should—' Mrs Heaven ignored me.

'Hungry are you you little terror you little wretch, hungry eh? We'll give you hungry eh mum arf a pound of tuppenny rice arf a pound of treacle—'

'WaaaaaaAAAAAAAAAA!'

'That's the way the money goes POP goes the weasel!'

'LAAAAAAAHAAAAAAAAR!'

I darted up and seized poor Beano back. But, oh
201

God, she smelt of Mrs Heaven. There was a weasel in the strawberry patch. Should I clasp her to my bosom all that recklessly? In came Van Dyke with three smoking coffees and his most charming smile.

'This is Mrs Heaven,' I warned. 'She was just telling me about all the accidents her boys have had.'

'Gor love me dear that ent nothing. Wayne put a nail froo 'is 'ead last week we'ad to take 'im down to Casualty, and while we was there Darren went straight into one of them plate glass windows—.' It took fifteen minutes for the coffee to decline from boiling point to a temperature which only took the skin off your lips. There was no shortage of conversation, however. Mrs Heaven confided to us further evidence of her appalling maternal negligence and predatory interest in our babe.

We went on smiling and nodding and sympathizing away like mad. Treacherous bastards, the middle classes. They go on smiling charmingly at you and then the minute they shut the door behind you it's—

'Good God! Oepen the windows! Ijt is unbearable!'

'It's everywhere! Do you think we'll have to shampoo the carpet to get rid of the smell? Dear, oh dear! Not a bit Gloucestershire, was she?'

It took us several hours of serious cleaning to banish the last traces of our cleaning woman. The smell of Heaven hung about in the hall for several days, though. I think it had seeped into the flagstones, like acid rain.

We interviewed several more people, with the windows open and with carefully tepid coffee. Van Dyke was instructed to test it with his elbow before bringing it in out of the kitchen. As the result of these interviews, we appointed several cleaning women. Not all at once: one after another.

The first one smelt pleasant and said little, and therefore seemed unimaginably suitable. But alas, she was of the projectile school of domestic work. She only had to open a door for the door handle to fly across the room and hit me between the shoulder blades. She turned on the tap, and the pipes snapped. The expensive vacuum cleaner filled up, mysteriously, with mud. Anyone can drop a cup and smash it – but she dropped the fridge and smashed it.

'We're getting an au pair girl,' I told her with deep regret. 'I'm so sorry. Van Dyke's niece is coming over for a year to learn English. So we won't need you after this week. What a shame.'

The second one left a film over everything. She left films of grease over the washing up. Films of dead flies over the windows. Films of white all over the dark surfaces, and films of black over all the white surfaces. She had not grasped the notion of rinsing, without which life is hollow and meaningless, not to mention grey and greasy. I cornered her as she was casting a film of scum over the wine glasses.

'I'm so sorry,' I said, 'but we've just heard that Van Dyke's niece is coming over from Holland. So we'll have a sort of au pair girl . . .'

Stroud is such a small town, I was sure all these cleaners would meet one day, if they didn't all know each other already. At least my lies were consistent. And if a Dutch au pair wasn't exactly imminent, at least Van Dyke's daughter would be coming for a week sooner or later. She might, at a distance, pass for an au pair, although the way she lay in the sun for hours, reading, might arouse suspicion. Never mind. We were already deeply into our third cleaner, Mrs Knowles.

Mrs Knowles's main disadvantage was her speed. She was due to clean for us for one and a half hours. But we soon found that she could do the washing up, scrub the floors, polish the brass and scour the utility room in seven and a half minutes. Soon we were fully involved in the business of inventing work for her.

'Could you perhaps ... polish the banisters? And then maybe you might like to ... dust the light bulbs?' Off she'd go like a bat out of hell, and I'd run into Van Dyke's room.

'Quick! Go and make a mess in the bathroom! I've run out of things for her to do and there's still forty minutes to go.' We had certainly been amply punished for our spinelessness in having to engage domestic help.

Indoors, now, some kind of cleaning activity was under way. But outdoors things were worse than ever. The weeds were choking the forsythia, and the forsythia was strangling what Van Dyke calls the Victorian Plum Tree. As for the elderly flower bush, it was well into a second childhood. I was deeply ashamed. What must the neighbours think?

Sidney Arbour wouldn't mind. For her the garden was a place to sit and read feminist novels, forget to pick currants and put up a tent for the girls. But Jack and Jill on the other side grew every variety of fruit and flowers known to man. How they remained friendly and cheerful as the clouds of weed-seeds drifted over the hedge I shall never know.

I engaged a gardener. Actually he rang me up to inquire about the cleaner's job, but on hearing it was no longer available, he offered his services in any other field I cared to mention. I instantly thought of the field outside the back door.

'When can you start?' I asked.

'How about in about ten minutes?' This sounded promising. His name was Antony. A nice name.

He looked promising, too: a sturdy English plough-boy sort of youth, with square-set shoulders and reassuringly tweedy, woolly sort of clothes. Obviously a misfit in his generation – the rest of whom were all wearing black vinyl and heavy-gauge machinery – he might be just the kind of eccentric to make a good gardener. He started to dig. I thought I'd

204

offer him a cup of tea now, before I went upstairs to start work.

'Tell you what,' he meditated, with wrinkled brow, after some half a minute's consideration of my offer, 'I don't really want anything yet. I'd like it in about half an hour, say. And I don't really like tea. Could I have a pint of orange squash? That'll do me.' There was, of course, not a single cc of orange squash in the house. I'd have to dart down to the shop to get some, in between inventing jobs for Mrs Knowles.

'Incidentally,' he remarked, as I turned to go, 'what do you think of Wagner?' His transistor, delicately balanced on the compost heap, was discreetly whispering some turgid waves of sound.

'Some people say he's a bit of a Fascist,' continued the dogged youth, 'but I don't know. What is Fascism, exactly, would you say?' My heart sank right through the rockery.

'You'll have to ask Van Dyke,' I shrugged. 'He's much more of an intellectual than I am. And he knows all about music. He's a composer.' Antony's eyes lit up, and I bit my tongue. Cursing myself for a total idiot, I ran indoors. The sheets of virgin-white paper lay waiting upstairs, waiting in vain for a pen to go waltzing across them. But first I had to waltz down to the shop for that orange squash, and warn Van Dyke about the philosopher at the bottom of the garden. Mrs Knowles appeared just as I was poised on the front doormat. 'I've finished polishing the skirting boards,' she beamed. 'Anything else I can do?'

We were not finished yet, alas. We still had to find a part-time nanny. Yet another advertisement went into the *Stroud News & Journal*, and a whole succession of school-leavers came to be interviewed. A new form of anguish broke upon us: the anguish of interviewing the catastrophically shy. They were all pink, washed and dressed in carefully ironed dainty white blouses through which their palpitating young hearts could mainly be heard. They accepted the offer of a cup of coffee, and then regretted it. It only drew attention to their shaking fingers and there was also the problem of how to organize the drinking of coffee and the answering of questions. Alternating these activities was obviously desirable, but proved strangely elusive.

My response to all this tension was to pretend to be outrageously relaxed myself and hope it would be infectious. I burped, scratched myself and yawned hideously like an ape.

'Have you had any experience of taking care of children, sort of thing, Jeannette?'

'Er . . . my little cousin. And our Carol's Darrel.'

'Have you really? Crumbs, that's terrific. I bet you're ever so experienced, then. What did you, you know, er, learn?' I picked my nose and laid my head on the table to show how relaxed I was. Jeannette quivered slightly beneath her neat, shiny hair.

'Er, they was . . . er, different.'

'I'll bet they bloody were! Kids *are* different, aren't they? Take our baby here. She's incredibly, amazingly different. I mean, I was expecting her to sleep all the time, and do you know, she never sleeps much at all. Crumbs, that put the wind up us, I can tell you. I bet that wouldn't have thrown you, though, eh, Jeannette? I bet you've got lots of experience playing with kids, eh? Do you play much with Carol's Darrel?'

'Er . . . yes, a bit.'

'What sort of games do they play at that age? What age *is* Carol's Darrel, by the way?'

'Er . . .' Jeannette went red. Was she, oh, hell, inventing Carol's Darrel as evidence of previous experience? I threw my legs up on to the dresser to show how relaxed I was (and nearly gave myself a hernia. It was further than I thought) and spat reassuringly into a pot of begonias. She must feel at home by now, dammit.

206

'Hard to keep track of how old they are, isn't it? They grow up so fast, don't they? I expect Carol's Darrel is about eighteen months, isn't he? That's about the age when you start to lose track of how old they are, isn't it? Although, blooming heck, I'm damned if I can remember how old our baby is, come to think of it. How old is she, now, love?' – to Van Dyke, whose head was buried in his hands, the lucky blighter – 'Is she three and a half months, now? Or is it weeks?'

In the end, Jeannette went. But not before we were all worn out with relaxation.

'My God!' I groaned to Van Dyke. 'I don't know about you, but I'm so tense, after all that, I'm going to have a bath.'

'You can't,' he objected. 'The next one ijs coming in ten minutes.'

In the end, we didn't take any of them; poor hopeful, shy, jobless girls. May they find a better employer than I would have been. In the end, my doctor recommended her ex-nanny, who was working at a nursery school in the mornings, and wanted a job in the afternoons. She was very experienced, in her mid-twenties, and called after another of my literary heroines: Jane Austen's Elizabeth Bennett.

When we opened our door to her, it was like seeing a daffodil standing there: she was so pretty and confident and friendly. She immediately put us at our ease and there was no need for relaxation. You can always tell, in my experience, within the first two seconds of opening the door. The interview's a waste of time for both parties.

'We won't bother with an interview,' I shall say next time. 'Just come up the path, ring the doorbell, and wait long enough for us to take a peep at you through the letter box. We'll let you know.' So Elizabeth Bennett came in the afternoons to take care of Beano, to give Van Dyke time to finish his *Organ Jets* and myself the chance to start my next book. I found it hard, though. If I could hear Beano chuckling away with Elizabeth, I wanted to run down and join in. If I could hear her crying, I wanted to run down and clasp her to my bosom – although nowadays full breast-feeding had given way to the bottle, which Beano pulled at in a greedy, careless way, like a tramp with a bottle of cider.

She also ate soft pappy things on spoons. 'HOK!' she had cried in alarm when first invited to taste the baby rice. Since it looks like wallpaper paste, I think HOK was putting it mildly. Soon, however, she got the hang of it all, and was greedily devouring everything in sight – especially envelopes.

The end of breast-feeding was a great relief. It was as if a weight had been lifted from my shoulders, and this was also quite literally true. My ample bosom shrank from its Apennine splendours until it was scarcely visible to the naked eye – my usual state. (Incidentally, when I was thirty-four an old friend with whom flirtatious badinage was the rule asked me *how old I actually was?*

'I'll give you a clue,' I giggled foolishly. 'My age and my bust measurement are exactly the same.' He hesitated for a few seconds in apparent perplexity, and then spoke.

'You can't be *that* young, surely.' So much for flirtation.)

But what was flirtation with mere men, compared with flirtation with my darling daughter? She had developed a deep, reluctant laugh: 'Hur . . . hur . . . hur!' Like a slow-witted Father Christmas. She was a bit slow, altogether. She still wasn't putting weight on fast enough for Them Down at t' Clinic, but now that she was drinking cows' milk and eating solid food and getting to be quite an Old Baby, they said there wasn't much point in weighing her so often any more. What had been the point of weighing her up till then? Answers on a postcard, please.

Beano still sucked away at me occasionally, but only for fun. 'Ooolie oolie ooo, num num num,' I whispered down at her. She stopped sucking and made a grab for my lips – in an attempt to shut them, I suppose.

I had baths with her, and gently soaped her delicate neck with its crumply skin, her wobbly head with its downy fuzz, her exquisite shoulder blades. When drying her, I placed my mouth on her proud little bot and blew hard. WHARP! went the skin. *Hur hur!* went the baby. So it seemed more than ever painful and odd to banish myself from this Paradise, hand her over to Elizabeth, and go up to my wretched study and write some more book.

When they went for walks I'd watch from my window as the pushchair disappeared off down the road, its white parasol diving and nodding like a flower in the wind above my baby's head. After fifteen minutes I was at the window again, craning and straining for their return. Three lines of book had been written, if I was lucky.

How had the parents of the past managed? Shakespeare, to start at the top? Well, he'd left home for twenty years, hadn't he? No wonder so many of his plays are about foolish old men being reunited with their darling daughters. But twenty years! Twenty minutes was about my limit. I counted the seconds till I could go downstairs and have tea with them. It was such fun down there. Why didn't I pay Elizabeth to write my books instead and look after the baby myself?

'How are you getting on with your boek?' inquired Van Dyke.

'Oh, you know. So on. Ooolie oolie oo! – I'll make a proper start next week.'

'But, Sue, next week we hav to go to Holland.'

'No, we don't. Surely not! It was July we were going to go to Holland.'

'Ijt is July.'

'It can't be! I've got to finish this book by the end of June.'

Beano discovered how to blow the food out of her mouth. (BLEEEEEEEEEEEK! BLLLLLLLLLLLLEEEEK!') I hoped they liked that sort of thing in Holland.

Chapter 21

Off we went across the North Sea. It seemed much easier than going to the Lake District, because we had done it before, I suppose. And it was good to know that Beano would not be crying for the breast every hour or so. Good heavens, I was strong enough to pack the baby rice and cough at the same time. I was curious to see the baby in the arms of her Dutch grandma, whom she so much resembled.

We were also to be reunited with Van Dyke's innumerable brothers and sisters and their many children, all living within a mile or so of the ancestral village, called something like 'SWeetabixabix. The idea was to stay with his family until we were totally exhausted, and then go to Amsterdam for a few days to recover. One of Van Dyke's compositions was also being performed. I expect it would take us a few days to recover from that, too.

The elder Van Dykes live in a large immaculate house in a large immaculate village. Van Dyke Senior used to be a market gardener and a local choirmaster, so music and gardening formed the main topics of conversation. What a shame I had not mastered any Dutch yet. Van Dyke's brother Ka dropped in on his way to deliver a load of swedes.

'Helloe moeder heloe vader helloe Soe, hej, Van D., jou ould bastoerd, hoe geos ijt?'

'Hij, Ka, thijs ijs Beatrix ouwer babje.'

'Wat a kuut kijd. Loets ov haar, toe. Wjat doe u uus, manuur?'

'Zitte doen voor a minuut, zon. Hav a bier. Hou waas kwijr-praktis laast nijt?'

'Aand have u stil goet aphijds on uur hoenijzukkel?'

'Ja, ja, de wifje trijd zprajijng dem bot sje hazzunt goot de nak.'

'Toornijps aar turifijk dis jaar.'

'Ja, Ij sauw you goot wan out de bak de sijs ov en elefantztoord.'

I found it rather soothing when I didn't have to try and understand. I could just switch off and let it all wash over me, while Beano romped on my knee. But there were times when my ignorance of the language and the culture let me down. Dinner, for example.

'Ij zupoes Ij'd beter goe doun de gaden en pik zom ztrawberrijs voor dijnner,' sighed Van Dyke's dad, stubbing out his third cigar.

'UUr klogs aar bei de bakdoor,' called his wife as he went. 'Ij moovd dem uit ov de utilijtij-roem bekos ov de stink.'

'Ja, dat wwas de pijg-schijt vrom de manuur-heep, sorrij.' Whilst he was busy in the garden, Van Dyke's mum made the dinner.

'Wat ijs voor dijner, moeder?' inquired Van Dyke.

'Veelbolls in soep, potajtoes en a bit of zalad,' she replied. 'En zstrawberrijs of coors.'

'Terrijjfik. Oj'll joost plaje a fju ov de Goldberg Variations, den, til ijt's reddij.'

As long as no one spoke to me, I was safe. Or was I? We sat poised at the dinner table, salivating at the sight of the vealballs swimming in their soup. Were they waiting for me to start? I grabbed my spoon and set to. 'Our Vader wijch aart in Heven—' Oh crumbs! Grace! Of course. They were as devout as they were decent. I pretended I had not really picked up my spoon to eat, only to swat at a passing fly. And there were plenty of them about, what with cows at the bottom of the garden.

'—thenks voor al de vood Jou zend uus, en blejst alzo be de Virgjin-Marie voor hoer effekt on de toornijps, wijch aar bludij marveloos dis jaar. Amen.'

'Hok!' cried Beano from her bouncing chair. She liked the look of those vealballs. Once you've got used to the novelty of Dutch food, it is very good. When I first saw Van Dyke's mum mixing soft-boiled egg with the lettuce, I had my doubts. But it was delicious. That's one thing I can say, in Dutch: *It is delicious.* I can also say, *the cow is tired, the pig is tired, the weather is fine* and *the honeysuckle is big.*

If you don't know much of a foreign language, the great thing is to dominate the conversation as much as possible. Don't let them get a word in. Then they won't be able to ask you one of those terrifying, mind-dazzling questions which leave you speechless and gaping and feeling a right Charlie. I used to dominate the conversation like anything while doing the washing up with Van Dyke's mother.

'The weather is fine,' I began. 'Delicious. But the pig is tired. The big pig. The big delicious pig is tired. The honeysuckle is as big as a cow, but not so delicious. It's good weather for tired cows . . .'

'Does you mum like me?' I whispered to Van Dyke in the depth of the night.

'Ja, she says you know your way to the sink.'

'What? Is that good?'

'Ja, it ijs a great kompliment.'

All the same, I couldn't help feeling what an advantage it was not to speak the same language as one's in-laws. There was half a chance they wouldn't

213

realize just how unsuitable I was.

We met the whole family: Ka, Mit, Sjep, Na, Fit, Blop, Wijp, Ga, Gus, Flip, Flop, Bla, Pus, and Astrid. Astrid was a baby and would probably end up as Id. She was Beano's younger cousin, and was the first baby I had seen who was smaller than Beano. How exquisitely sweet she was! I longed to cradle her funny little newborn old man's head. But there was no time. Bla and Pus had to rush off home to spray the kohl. So I cradled my own baby instead, which was even better.

'Shall we go for a walk?' I whispered. 'It's not raining, for once.'

'Hoh!'

So I got out her pushchair and strapped her into it. The sky was already going a bit grey again, so I'd dressed her in her waterproof suit, woollies and wellies. I scowled up at the sky. *With regard to this here baby,* I warned the clouds, *just don't get any big ideas rain-wise, hail-wise or otherwise, or it will be the last load you ever bloody drop.*

All the same, we were only about halfway from 'SWeetabixabix to Krumhoorn when the heavens opened. On each side, as far as I could see, the rows of cabbages and spinach stretched away to the grey horizon. I turned back. The rain was trickling down my neck. I was pushing a pushchair along suburban streets, for God's sake. I felt like a mother imperson-ator: someone playing mummies and daddies. In every garden I passed the drenched marigolds stood to attention, not daring to rampage, especially on Sunday. And yet . . . And yet . . .

Could it be that I was not the same person who, two years ago, had cultivated old roses and younger men? Who, at the first whiff of dependence, would zoom off leaving the younger man to cool his heels?

'Your trouble,' one of them said to me once, in the middle of what I hoped would be a polite and orderly dissolution, 'is that you're never prepared to take responsibility for anybody.' I acknowledged the truth of this accusation. The slightest hint of need, and I would make an excuse and escape to the Deepest West End of Town. And was this really the same person, pushing a pushchair through soaked suburbia, and beyond that, cabbages and more cabbages, all very, very wet?

'Huerk!' objected Beano, as the first rain percolated through her woolly hat and reached her semi-bald dome. Lucky old rain!

'My darling!' I cried, kneeling before her in a puddle. 'Are you wet and miserable, then? Cheer up, my little pickled walnut, life is not so bad as it seems. When we get home I will show you a photograph of Tuscany, where the sun shines.'

'Naaaa! Naaaa! 'LAAAAAR!'

'Yes, I know it's raining, but this is your heritage. What is rain anyway but drink for the plants? Dearest baby, do not fret: we are nearly home, and when we get there you shall have a real strawberry from your grandpa's garden.'

'Naaaaaaaaaaaaaarg!

We rattled home quickly over the last few metres of pavement. It's a shame they didn't have a bath, because we could both have jumped into that, but not even being wet to the skin could kill the curious contentment in me. I dried Beano's hair and it fluffed up on top of her head like a baby bird's just hatched from the egg. I fed her a mashed strawberry. She blew on it, loud and long, and got red juice all down her chin. 'BLLLLLLLLLLLLLLLLLLERT! HUR HUR!' We went for a walk to the window and looked out at the orderly flowerbeds.

'This is another sort of garden,' I pointed out. 'Nothing poisonous here. Nothing prickly. Look at the man on the bike. Listen! I can hear the bells.' She turned to me and sucked my cheek. It was still

215

raining, but contentment was rising within me like a giant sun.

There were still embarrassing moments, though. Van Dyke's concert proved to be a disaster. It was performed in Middelburg, a place far enough away for us to drive all morning to get there and book a room in a hotel for the night. Van Dyke was on edge. This work of his had never been performed before, and it was difficult.

The Japanese pianist had been practising since January, but the small orchestra had only been given their parts a couple of weeks ago. As a result, after three minutes the pianist was already leading by about six lengths. Poor Van Dyke writhed and groaned at my side as the wrong sound unfurled. The baby, ever sensitive to her parents' moods, began to howl. I carried her out into the lobby, which was full of strong single young people talking and smoking. They did not notice us, and there were no spare seats. I got tired of carrying Beano about in the smoke, so we ventured outdoors. It was dark and raining, with a gale blowing straight off the North Sea.

'Come on, Beano,' I whispered. 'Let's go and find a nice warm café until Daddy's concert is finished.' That, unfortunately, would be rather a long time, since after the concert there was to be a discussion between composers, performers and the audience. I had two hours to kill. But I was also extremely hungry. A gust of rain smacked into our faces. 'HOK!' I pulled her hood down over her eyes, and held my waterproof jacket around her. Just one little dark eye peeped out into this bleakest of nights, as we walked the streets together.

The cafés were all shut, or full, or diabolically noisy and smoky. After a while I got that feeling you get when you know you're never going to find anywhere suitable. I could not go back to the hotel as I did not know the way, and we had come by car, anyway, so it was probably miles away.

'Never mind, dear baby,' I sang to her. 'With a hey, ho, the wind and the rain. You're safe with me and I'm safe with you. For the rain it raineth every day.'

We loitered under a draughty awning. Nearby some youths were hanging around in a kind of amusement arcade; propositioning and flirting with some girls. How long ago all that seemed. And how unappealing. Nobody noticed the middle-aged woman dripping in the shadows with the baby slung against her breast. Nobody ogled, leered, or bothered me. I had, I suddenly realized, become invisible to men. Not just tonight: for months previously. And do you know what? I hadn't even noticed. 'Laaaaaaaa-rrrrrm!' murmured Beano.

I walked on a bit, and found a little old arcade, totally hidden and dark, where I leaned against the wall and let the baby feed. The wind rushed up and down; the rain blasted in gusts against the stone: we were somehow sheltered from it all. Eventually, she slept against my heart: my trusty breastplate against the worst of blackness, wind and boiling storm. Her mouth hung open slightly, upwards, as if she was about to speak. A scent came from it like a warm garden.

Chapter 22

Back in Gloucestershire, it was still raining, only rather more gently.

'I don't know how to tell you this ...' began Elizabeth Bennett, looking both pleased and guilty. We braced ourselves for the inevitable. Once you've found the perfect nanny she always, somehow, disappears.

'I've been offered this job ... I applied for it months ago. Long before I started coming to you ... I'd forgotten all about it, but a few days ago they rang me up and asked me to go for an interview ... and well ... they wanted me.'

She had to take it, of course. It was a great opportunity: working with problem families, advising them on the welfare of their young children, and fostering the idea of progress through play.

We waved her goodbye, and off I went once more to the newspaper office. 'Part-time nanny ...' etc, etc. Beano was with me in her pushchair. On the way home the sun came out for a fraction of a second, right in her face, and she screamed in alarm. It put the fear of God into me, too, for a minute or two. I'd almost forgotten what it was.

'We'll get you a nice new nanny,' I promised, rubbing my dry worn old cheek against her moist round new one, as we danced to Bob Marley's haziest reggae, upstairs in the attic. A few sunbeams fell on to the carpet, so we rolled in them.

'Hur hur hur!'

'You are my cub,' I confided, 'and I shall lick you if I like.' I licked her under the chin. 'HUR HUR HUR HUR!' Yes, despite the many uglinesses of the planet, its cruelties and mortalities, we rolled in the light, back then.

Before she learnt to push me away and walk off, proud of her independence; before she gave her deepest smiles and her racing heart to another, unknown and elsewhere; before she pulled herself up into the world, treading me down into my hole, as is her destiny; before she knew me as an individual, and a silly, fearful one at that; before she could understand jokes or avoid kisses – before she even knew they were kisses – they rained down on her eggshell skull and the strange little nut of her nose, and her laughter rang out like the bravest music – before she even knew it was laughter.

Some people answered the advertisement. There were some nannies left to choose from, it seemed. Once again, one glimpse of Miss Sandra Oak on the doorstep, and we knew it would be all right. Shy and eighteen, Sandra could nevertheless smile through solid concrete. Such a smile! She was pretty, plump and a Methodist – like both the heroines of *Adam Bede* put together.

She told us she was lazy and untidy, which was a bit of a relief, since she otherwise seemed full of charm and grace. Only one thing stood between us and perfect happiness: she was only available until September, when she was to start a full-time Nursery Nursing course at the local Tech.

'Still,' she said, 'if you like, my mum could give

you a hand after that.' It emerged that Sandra's mum had been a foster-mother for many years.

'I expect she's had a lot of experience of young babies, then?'

'Oh, yes,' nodded Sandra. 'About a hundred, I should think.'

Mrs Oak came down to inspect us. She was a no-nonsense, sturdy, old-fashioned matron of immense dignity. We all had tea in the garden, under the plum tree. 'I don't like these wasps,' said Mrs Oak. 'I don't like them at all.'

There was not an ounce of pastoral nonsense about her. Antony, who had been defoliating large areas of ground elder in the deep recesses of the lower garden, joined us for his pint of squash and a piece of cake.

'Hello!' he nodded to the group at large. 'You know, I've been reading a lot of Lawrence lately. What's your opinion of Lawrence, Sue? With regard to his sexual philosophy, I mean.'

'Oh, I don't know, Antony. I can't remember any more.'

'Virginia Woolf didn't like him, did she? But then, wasn't she a bit of a – well, I hope you don't mind my saying so, but a bit of a lesbian?' Mrs Oak dusted the cake crumbs off her knee. Sandra stared at her sandals.

'I never hold with eating outdoors,' said Mrs Oak. 'It do always create more trouble than it's worth.' She lifted Beano onto her knee.

'It is nice, sometimes, though, don't you think, Mrs Oak? For a special occasion.'

'But there again . . .' Antony took another slice of cake and chewed slowly, staring out towards the distant Severn plain. 'I do think Lawrence had a point. I mean, I believe that men should be masculine and women feminine, sort of thing. Or is that too Fascist? What do you think?'

'Who's a giggly girl, then?' Mrs Oak addressed Beano, shaking her playfully from side to side. 'You are. Yes, you are! Yes, you are!' Beano giggled helplessly.

'You see, I'm a bit concerned about the feminine side of my nature. I mean, I don't want to give you the wrong impression, but . . .'

'There's nothing to fear from the feminine side of your nature, Antony,' I encouraged him. 'Look at Van Dyke. No one could say he's effeminate. And yet he does the shopping and the cooking and the cleaning, and all his share of the baby business.'

'Does he, now?' asked Mrs Oak, giving me a sharp look.

'It ijs different in Holland,' explained Van Dyke, flicking a tea bag daintily into the hedge.

'Do you think I ought to go to Holland?' inquired Antony. 'I want to be a writer, really, because if you don't mind my saying so, I think I'm quite good at it. But I sometimes think I ought to broaden my horizons a bit. What do you think?'

'Cover that milk, Sandra: things'll be dropping into it.'

'I think you ought to go to Venezuela,' I said, perhaps a little too urgently. Antony squinted at me suspiciously. 'Really? Seriously?'

'Yes. I do. If I were a young man with no ties, no obligations, in good health, willing to work his passage, I'd go off to South America this minute.'

'Did you travel much when you were – um – young? Don't get me wrong: I don't mean you're not young now! Did you, though?'

'Not really. And I'm not young now, thank goodness.'

'Don't you regret it, though? I mean, don't you think it might have expanded your horizons as a writer? I mean, don't you feel trapped by having a child and everything?'

'Not at all. I feel freed, as a matter of fact.'

'Did Lawrence have a child? Or do you think he was really a suppressed homosexual?'

Mrs Oak rose from her seat. 'I must be going,' she announced. 'I have the Over Sixties teas to see to.'

Remarkably, Mrs Oak agreed to take over in Sandra's place when September came. By then Antony had gone off to a northern polytechnic, which although not offering the potential for mind expansion enjoyed by Venezuela, was at least elsewhere.

On the first day that Mrs Oak was due, I spent most of the morning in frenzied cleaning and tidying. Only then did I realize the bitter truth: there are two sorts of domestic help. Those that you clean up after, and those that you clean up before. Mrs Oak arrived, put down her shopping bag, and looked around. 'I thought I'd take her for a walk,' she suggested. 'But perhaps I'd better just create a bit of order here first.'

She glanced at the kitchen floor, which had escaped my earlier attentions. 'Have you done the floor yet today, Sue?' *Yet today!* What tact! And what gentle educational pressure! Mrs Oak had been trained for domestic service forty years ago. This meant that she could simultaneously keep Beano amused, put me in my place and iron Van Dyke's shirts so they looked like Japanese paper flowers, beautifully folded.

Mrs Oak didn't ever venture into the back garden again, and I could hardly blame her. Over a year's neglect had changed it from Winnie Windbreaker's bee-thronged paradise into a steep rough bank overgrown with coarse grass, nettles and brambles. Weeds were romping through the border, strangling and choking the dainty and delightful plants. We had repeatedly let the lawn shoot skywards and then hacked at it in panic, so it looked bruised and confused. It had been such a damp summer that many of the plums had gone mouldy on the stalk. I

222

wandered through the desolation with a melancholy sense that it was all my fault, even the rain.

Antony had done his best. But since I'd been too busy to supervise him properly, and too preoccupied to notice at first the limits of his horticultural sense, it turned out that I had been paying him good money to pull up the paeonies, strip off the topsoil and carry it out into the street, and introduce a vast array of perennial weed roots into the helpless borders. If only I didn't feel so weak! But months and months of broken nights had taken their toll. And besides, I was only too aware that Mrs Oak's role was to free me for real work: the earning of bread and butter, not the digging-out of ground elder roots.

'I'm sorry. I'm sorry,' I murmured to the garden, and slipped back indoors. I knew it thought I didn't love it. This was the second summer I'd done no gardening. It filled me with guilt and grief.

Beano was blossoming, though. I suppose she was my garden at the moment. Her neck smelt of nectar and her breath of strawberries. Her skin shone with the soft white gleam of a lily in the dusk. And her face was covered with compost most of the time. Until Mrs Oak took over, of course. Mrs Oak mopped away the grime on Beano's cheek, and wiped her nose before it even had a chance to think about running. Beano had never been so clean.

A cheque dropped into the void: a Tax Rebate for £800. I knew very well that Sod's Law dictated that every Tax Rebate is followed by a Tax Demand for twice as much. But I ignored this. Clutching my cheque to my heart, I picked up the phone and dialled Graduate Gardeners of Bisley. There was something spuriously reassuring about that word *graduate*. I had a feeling they would not pull up the paeonies or remove the topsoil. And if they did, I could demand to see their diplomas and tear them up on the spot.

They sent round another Antony. But this one was

223

different. He proved to be, as it were, St Antony. He had the physique of Michelangelo's David (decently clothed in earthy green gardening clothes, of course). He had the gentlest manner in the world and was so soft-spoken, his voice sort of hung on the air like the scent of violets. He was, in fact, well on the way to being a plant himself: and what higher praise can one bestow? We walked up the grassy bank, with me apologizing all the while as if it was his garden I'd been neglecting. And as it turned out, in a way it was.

The first priority was access. You simply couldn't get up to the top of the garden without pushing your way through prickly thickets and spraining your ankle, or, if a nasty chunk of limestone gave way, tumbling into the void. It was almost a sheer precipice from the shade of the plum tree at the top to the concrete outside the back door at the bottom. Many of my loved ones were getting on in years, or still at the toddling dawn of life, and though in Christian iconography the Garden is irrevocably associated with the Fall, I was not keen for this to be acted out by my own flesh and blood.

I wanted a series of paths and steps. St Antony suggested making them out of old railway sleepers and gravel. This immediately cheered me up. It was a kind of invisible coded message, rather like a Masonic handshake, guaranteeing a sympathetic approach. Old railway sleepers! Already I could see myself perched on one, Beano fingering the tarry bits while I travelled in my imagination down long-abandoned branch lines to places such as Adlestrop or Ottery St Mary.

I'd had vague yearnings about putting the garden in order: St Antony translated them into imaginative detail, and when his estimate arrived it proved to be exactly the same amount as my tax rebate. So I watched, in a fever of excitement, from the bathroom window as St Antony (ably assisted by the Blessed

Bert) flung himself at the terrain. Soon the rough bank, which had been so steep and wild 'twas only fit for baboons to congregate upon, gradually assumed a shape. Wide, generous curvings led the eye up; gravel gleamed gold; the steps marched importantly up the middle, formal and strong, like the bass in a piece of music.

They levelled, smoothed and blasted the other Antony's seed-infested heap off the face of the earth: they laid, with turf, a pretty little oval lawn in the lower part of the garden, around which deep borders were dug, awaiting my planting. I stood transfixed at the bathroom window, grinding my teeth and blushing in furious pleasure. There I would have a white tree-paeony! There, a blue sprawl of ceanothus! And beyond, a clump of scented this-and-that! And some whossname with white undersides of leaves that would flash when seen from below.

Oh golly! I ran downstairs to make them a cup of tea. Another cup of tea. I made them at half-hourly intervals to show my gratitude. St Antony revealed his sanctity not only by his aesthetic sense, superhuman strength and unfailing sweetness of temper, even when rain was trickling down his neck ('We're dissolving!' he grinned), but also by the way he did all sorts of extra things not mentioned in the estimate. He pruned a tree here, he rebuilt a wall there, he carted away all our shameful rubbish without a murmur of displeasure. And when he'd finished he not only swept the path behind him but *weeded the edges of it as well*.

Our neighbours Jack and Jill admired the work, though Jack cast a rather satirical eye at the railway sleepers. 'What time does the three-fifteen come through?' he inquired. As I looked up at the lovely design of the garden, now proud of itself with its curves and gleams and rhythmical steps, something unknotted itself deep in my heart, and I felt my

225

senses swim with the warm pleasure of feeling at home – at last.

St Antony had translated my intuitions into reality, doing the work as if it was his own loved garden. Perhaps back in the golden age all craftsmen were like that. I would plant my Eden in the spring. But now, at last, I could get down to work – real work, work with a heart at peace and at home. I'd just have a brief glance at those plant catalogues first.

Chapter 23

Work! So long had passed without our doing any that a faint sheen of glamour hung about the very word. Van Dyke had to get to grips with a composition for two rather unusual wind instruments: the bass clarinet and the contrabass (i.e. double bass) flute. These instruments are both so low and breathy that they are scarcely audible to the human ear, and even when they are, can easily be mistaken for a sigh, or worse, from one of the family pets.

A couple of talented Dutch musicians, however, had been attracted to these instruments – perhaps because of the national fascination with drains. I'm sure if one blew gently down a sewer pipe (a nice clean one, I mean), one could make no end of strange musicks i'the earth, causing panic in the housing estates and a rumour that the god Hercules was prowling about again and might pop up and make trouble at any time.

Van Dyke was very excited by this commission, so he seized his slide rule and table of logarithms and made a curious graph on a very long piece of graph paper stretching right across the room. It looked a bit like the National Debt, or a statistical analysis of voting patterns in the Philippines, but it was, Van Dyke informed me, the conceptual framework for *Athena Keramitis*. He had evidently progressed beyond soup and towards goddesses. I couldn't help feeling this was a bit of a mistake.

The days passed, and Van Dyke disappeared regularly into his room for long periods and re-emerged with blackened brows. I suppose writing for bass clarinet and contrabass flute was, as it were, rather a long way down. I wondered whether Van Dyke should apply for membership of the National Union of Mineworkers.

'How's *Athena Keramitis*?' I asked. (By the way, I didn't realize she had a surname, did you? I didn't think gods bothered with that sort of thing. Athena Keramitis. I think she keeps a delicatessen in North London.)

'Oh, it ijs OK,' said Van Dyke, warming his hands around a mug of raspberry leaf tea (it was left over from my pregnancy, but could still help, we felt, at moments of intense creative labour). 'I have made some more kalkulations and diagrams.' More calculations and diagrams? This information unnerved me slightly. Of course, music is closely allied to mathematics, but I was beginning to feel that if he went on like this, we might end up hearing not sweet airs which give delight, but the sound of splitting atoms.

'Can I have a look?' I asked. Van Dyke showed me his new diagrams. One was beautifully coloured in blue and pink and would have made a very pretty bed cover. Another looked like the heart-monitor print-out from Beano's birth. It was hard to see how these documents might relate to music, but I was sure Van Dyke knew what he was doing.

However, Van Dyke did not share my confidence. A few more days passed and he began to feel terribly tired. He had a little nap at 11.30 a.m., then another at 3.30 p.m., dozed on the sofa during the 6 o'clock news, and went to bed at 9 p.m. What was wrong? Was it the sleeping sickness, like the fat boy in Dickens? Was he going to slide gracefully into a coma and not wake up for twenty years – just in time for Beano's wedding?

'Van Dyke!' I cried, the moment his eyes flickered towards consciousness for a split second. 'How's *Athena Keramitis*?'

'Ah,' he yawned. 'It ijs OK. I am reading a very useful book that will help me very much in the piece's structure.'

'What book is that?' It was *The Self-Organizing Universe: Scientific and Human Implications of the Emerging Paradigm of Evolution*. No wonder he'd felt unusually tired. Just reading the title made me feel faint.

Next day I caught Van Dyke looking morose and rubbing his leg thoughtfully against the radiator. This was a striking departure from his usual cheerful habits. 'What's the matter?'

'I am stuck with my piece.' Ah! At last.

When people at parties find out you're a writer or a composer they usually say, 'You must have such self-discipline! I couldn't possibly sit down and work if I was at home all day. I have to go off to the office and know there's a boss watching me or I wouldn't do anything at all. How do you manage it?'

It's not like that at all, of course.

For a start, you don't need self-discipline if you've got a mortgage and twelve Standing Orders at the bank. Sheer terror propels you towards your work. And if it's going well, you can't keep away in any case. But at times like this: getting stuck, and worst of all, getting stuck at the beginning, well, anything in the world is preferable to that desk and that sheet of empty paper.

At such times I clean the lavatories: even the outdoor lavatory with its decades of slime and gunge. I scrub the kitchen floor – on my knees, with a toothbrush, because it takes longer that way. I vacuum under the beds, on top of the wardrobes, between the banisters and behind the fridge. And I polish the piano – from below.

The house is never cleaner than when I'm stuck with my work. And I sit amidst the sparkle and order with a face like thunder, biting my nails and turning the pages of a woman's magazine in an anguish of paralysis.

So my heart bled for poor Van Dyke. But I would help him. *Take an interest in his work*, the women's magazines all urge. Thank goodness he wasn't a stockbroker then. I wouldn't find it easy to work up much enthusiasm about stockbroking, though I suppose I could've dressed up in fishnet tights and a bowler and danced in singing 'Money Makes The World Go Round' just like the girls in *Cabaret*.

It wasn't hard to take an interest in Van Dyke's work. But I wasn't sure how best to help him out of his present impasse.

'Let's go for a walk!' I cried, and spirited him up onto the wolds, Beano slung over his shoulders. A cloud of birds wheeled over the hedge, performed a figure eight, and then streamed off over the fields.

'Did you hear that?' I cried. 'The sound of their wings? Wasn't that interesting – rhythmically speaking!'

'Beah!' A sheep spoke.

'Listen to those sheep! Terrific, aren't they? So random in their – er – pattern of sounds. And the variation of pitch, too!'

'Have you brought some apples?' inquired Van Dyke, trying to give my mouth something else to do. We bit, juicily, into Granny Smiths (incidentally, she must have been a sour old bag, mustn't she?) and trudged on up the footpath.

'Hey! The sound our teeth made biting the apple! A sort of crisp explosion! And underneath it all, the rhythmic plod plod plod of our feet! You could call it Paradise Lost!'

Beano woke up and gave a mournful cry. She always senses when things are not quite right. 'The cry of the baby! Now, that was quite a deep note! Could you get that note on a contrabass flute?'

At this point, mercifully, I tripped on a lump of limestone, gasped, inhaled one of Granny Smith's sourest mouthfuls and almost choked to death. I interpreted it as a sign from Athena Keramitis to keep my trap shut.

A couple of days later, a kind of invisible, intangible shudder ran through the house. So intangible that I didn't actually notice it at first. But all the hairs on the cat went curly for a split second, and the yoghurts heaved briefly in their pots deep in the fridge. Yes, the goddess had landed. You could feel the skid-marks all down your spine. Presently Van Dyke skipped gaily from his room and tossed the baby several times into orbit. 'Would you like a pankake, darling?' So things were all right. On course. The Dutch musicians, who were both called Harry, would get their goddess after all.

Van Dyke was still working on commissions for Dutch musicians because of a quite staggering xenophobia demonstrated by the English musical establishment. On his arrival in England he had written a whole shoal of letters to various musical institutions: to orchestras, quartets, colleges, festivals, etc., enclosing a curriculum vitae, offering his services and seeking to make contact with English musical life. Or, as I have come to think of it, English musical death.

Van Dyke received, in answer to his tide of introduction, at most a couple of polite 'We'll keep your name on our files' replies. I grew more and more embarrassed at the sheer rudeness and indifference of my fellow countrymen. The contemporary music scene, it seemed, was dog eat dog, and unless your emigré husband happened to be a chic dissident with the snow of Siberia on his shoulders, they didn't want to know. It was a year before Van Dyke received a friendly and helpful reply to any of his letters. It only proved, to me, the all-pervasive truth of Sod's Law: that if you offer yourself to people, they never want you, and if you ignore them, they beat a path to your door.

I myself was experiencing the reverse thrust of this law. Having spent years writing to newspapers, magazines, television companies and radio networks, offering them plays, stories, articles, ideas – a cornucopia of creative endeavour – and having received at most a rather snotty acknowledgment and usually no more than a howling silence, I had retired to my den, had a baby and lost all interest in work. And what happened? The phone started to ring. Could I write for this TV programme, for that radio programme: review this book, dash off such and such a radio series?

Well, I suppose I had to. I girded up my loins and faced the first of my challenges: reviewing a play for the arts programme *Kaleidoscope*. All I had to do was go to London, watch the play, think what to say, get up in the morning, go to the BBC and say it. Fancy getting paid for that! Why, it was just like real life used to be. Harriet, a girlfriend I hadn't seen for ages, offered me a bed for the night in exciting – perhaps a little too exciting – Ladbroke Grove. Still, I could take a taxi there after the theatre. Nobody ever got mugged and raped actually *inside a taxi*, did they?

I kissed Beano goodbye on her pale dome and skipped off to the station. London! The blood was tingling in my veins. On the train I stared out at the gas-holders of Ruislip with eager anticipation. Paddington! Soot! Fog! No, wait a minute, that was going too far back – to the childhood trips to London: the steam train, the Natural History Museum, Hamley's toy shop, a taxi to the station (in the days when taxis had those funny little opaque horn-like windows at the back – but wait – whose childhood was this? Mine or Grandma's?).

I felt a sense of childlike excitement, certainly, as I made my way to the Royal Court Theatre, collected the tickets, and met my friend Raymond who was to accompany me. And so we got stuck into the play: *The Grace of Mary Traverse* by Timberlake Wertembaker. Timberlake Wertembaker sounds like a wholefood holiday camp in Canada but is in fact a very sharp-brained woman who writes plays that are bristling with ideas. In fact, the childhood excitement began to give way to a rising panic as I realized that I couldn't keep up with her, intellectually, at all. She was cruising along in her Rolls-Royce and all I had was roller skates and rusty ones at that.

If only it had been a familiar old play like *King Lear*, I could have relaxed a bit and focused instead on things like performance and pace and all that stuff. But crumbs, I couldn't even quite follow the plot. In fact, *was* there a plot? Luckily they were selling copies of the play in the foyer and I was already fingering mine as I watched. How long would it take to read? Could I hope to get to bed by, say, 3 a.m.?

'Raymond!' I hissed as we milled out into the dark streets. 'What was it about? What shall I say?'

Raymond is nothing if not brilliant and articulate, and as we ate a quick post-theatre supper, he reeled off a glittering analysis of it all. But in the taxi on the way to Harriet's, I found that Raymond's sparkling critique was slipping away down the gaps in my mind, like drops of mercury between the floorboards. Had I always had such gaps? Or was it just the after-effects of Beano? Had she left me with less mind than I used to have, as well as more body?

'Hello!' cried Harriet, emerging from her elegant

233

bunker (known as a garden flat) and welcoming me down into it with all her wonderful old upper-middle-class fervour. It was midnight. Would I like a cup of tea? And guess who was here: Lois. Not Lois! I hadn't seen her since university, and to be honest, I'd hardly seen her even then. Now she was working with a radical theatre group. Fascinating!

It went on being fascinating until about 2.30 a.m., by which time my head had turned to oolite, complete with caverns and stalactites. What was wrong? I used to be able to do this sort of thing. This used to be my way of life, dammit. At 2.54 Lois left for home. We vowed not to leave it another fifteen years, although I expect we will. One's life is just so big, unfortunately. I've often wished mine was a size 18, but there you are.

'Good God!' shrieked Harriet. 'It's nearly 3 o'clock! You must go to bed! But first, do tell me — what's it like, having a baby?' Harriet was winding herself up to motherhood, so it seemed that the least I could do was give her a vague hint or two of the joys and tribulations in store.

'Good God! It's 4.30! We must go to bed! But how fascinating! Would you like another cup of tea?' I declined the tea, and dived instead into her large sofa.

'I'm not asleep,' I kept thinking. 'I'm still not asleep. I'm definitely not asleep. And whatever am I going to say about that play? Oh God, I mustn't start to worry about what I'm going to say, or I really will never go to sleep at all. Good God! It's 5.30!! And I'm still not asleep! It's hardly worth going to sleep now, anyway. Oh dammit, I'll stop trying, and read the play instead.'

I fell asleep. And then, at 6.40: KLANG KER BLANG KER KLANG KR BLONK KER BANGGGLE! The dustbin men, those heralds of the dawn, had come to Ladbroke Grove.

I got up and after four cups of tea and some toast to soak it up, and a brief last-minute skip through the playtext, I climbed into another taxi to Broadcasting House. It seemed reckless using all these taxis, but last night I'd been in danger of losing my purse or my life and this morning it was my consciousness.

Luckily my exhaustion was so comprehensive, I was too tired to reach for my adrenalin, and when they asked me about the play, a strange thing happened. My mouth opened and began to speak – by itself, as it were. I crouched behind some rocks (I think they used to be my head) and let my mouth do its stuff.

'Thank you, mouth,' I croaked in the next taxi on the way to the station, and shoved a big bar of chocolate into it as a reward. God knows what it had said. But then, who cared? Slumped in a corner seat on the homeward train, I greeted the Cotswold hillsides with an ache of longing.

'Still,' I commented to Van Dyke, 'I'll say this for it, as an experience: nothing could be more frightening than that.' Wrong again.

A few days later the phone rang. A deep, husky, Hungarian voice introduced itself as the producer of the BBC radio programme *Stop the Week* with Robert Robinson. Would I, perhaps, asked the Hungarian voice, be interested in taking part? Oh yes, I twittered inanely, trying to ignore the black shadow that had fallen across my soul at this awful summons. The KGB, the angel of death, anything rather than *Stop the Week*.

'*Stop the Week*?' cried Tyger when I told her. 'I'd rather have an operation than be on *Stop the Week*.'

How many times I had listened to the programme, usually from the luxury of a Saturday night bath, and thought to myself, *Poor devils. Thank God I don't have to join in.* Then I'd sink further into the bath like a hippopotamus, revelling in my taciturnity, doing what I am happiest of all doing: steaming silently. I am, you see, terribly bad at talking. I can't even say, 'Excuse me,' to somebody in a crowded street without it all going awkward and setting the relationship off on the wrong foot.

Stop the Week, for those not acquainted with its unique formula, is like a chat show without the chat. The participants are usually professors and *bels esprits* if not *éminences grises*, and show how effortlessly clever they are by talking about frivolous things like False Teeth and Breakfast, in a furious, sententious and competitive way.

The programme's aim seems to be that they should all be shouting each other down in a scintillating and witty mêlée, until Robert Robinson plummets down from a great height like an osprey seizing a salmon and clinches the whole thing with the decisive snap of an epigram.

People either love it or hate it. Me, I adore it. I wouldn't miss it for anything. I find it compulsive, like watching a punch-up. But as for participating . . . the mere thought made me go hot and cold with sheer terror. Those brilliant wits and intellectual acrobats were way out of my league. Compared to theirs, my brains were cold porridge.

For a while I seriously wondered if they had got my name wrong and were thinking of somebody else. What, me? Dull, dazed, tongue-tied, tame, lame, Limb? Were they, perhaps, confusing me with Laetitia Limb, Professor of Crypto-Callisthenics at Cardiff University? It appeared not. The charming Hungarian voice continued to phone me up, asked me to have some thoughts on the subject of *Change*, and then murmured rather menacingly that he would see me tomorrow at 5 o'clock.

My first thoughts on the subject of Change were that I should change my name, address and telephone number and fly off to Rio tonight. But no. It was only a radio programme, dammit. It would all be over in forty minutes. It was WORK. If indeed you could call it work. To me it seemed something in another dimension – the dimension, say, of Ancient Rome. Maybe the guys about to be thrown to the lions had experienced just such palpitations as racked my ribcage now.

I tried to think about Change, honestly. I thought about it day and night. But whenever I got anywhere near it, the word somehow slipped away and – yes, changed into something else. After a while, because I'd thought about the word 'Change' so much, it went all strange, and rang on and on in my head like a Chinese bell. Still, I thought, it'll be all right on the night.

But it wasn't. When the night came I was more nervous than I had been for my Caesarian. I longed for an epidural – from the waist up. For half an hour before blast-off I loitered in a loo not far from Broadcasting House, alternately peeing and adjusting my appearance in a vain attempt to hide behind make-up. I put on three different lipsticks all at once, but even that did not make me look more intelligent. Would a touch of blusher bring the illusion of health to my ghostly cheeks? Or would that be too Coco the Clown?

But perhaps clown was my role. The producer had said that what he wanted was light-hearted anecdotes, which was just as well since that was all my life had yielded so far. Whenever there's a programme with three men and a woman, it's very strange being the one woman. You somehow start to sound frivolous and empty-headed even if you're talking about Wholeness and the Implicate Order. Perhaps it's the fluty pipe of the female voice. To counteract this, I had practised a deep growl, a bit like a Staffordshire Bull Terrier whose favourite tennis ball is being threatened.

And what would Robert Robinson be like in three dimensions? Perhaps he'd be mild and reassuring, pat me on the head, offer me a cup of tea and burble on about the weather. But one glance at the great man as he burst through the swing doors was enough to convince me that he was, if possible, even more deadly than on TV or radio, i.e. about as mild and reassuring as a guided missile. I could see that he didn't suffer fools at all, and I was under the impression that I was not just one but somehow several. A distillation of folly.

We sat down, our microphones were adjusted, and we taxied out along the tarmac. Compared with this, however, my fear of flying was a mere *frisson* of misgiving. I was so nervous that if I looked down I could see my jersey galloping madly over my frenzied little heart. My contact lenses were misting up, I wanted to be sick, and my mouth was stuck together with the three lipsticks.

But the moment had come. The men seized on poor old Change and tore it apart in a way that was far from frivolous and anecdotal. And then, suddenly, Robert Robinson turned to me, there was a split second of silence, my bra burst, my heart flew across the room and impaled itself upon a hatstand, and my mouth – miraculously, I have to believe – opened. They'd all been talking about Change in a resonant Renaissance sort of way and here I was gabbling on about being peed on by an aardvark. There's a flower called *Pulsatilla vulgaris*, and believe me, Ladies and Gentlemen, I was that flower.

Well. So this was work. In my simplicity I'd thought that by the time I was forty I would more or less know what I was doing, *vis à vis* occupation, and the stress levels would've gone down a bit. Nothing could be further from the truth. Here I was hurling myself recklessly into storm-tossed abysses of new experience, and emerging bloody and bowed. I'd imagined a gentle transition into the middle years: a paragraph of my novella ('Her eyes glistened in the lamplight as the wind howled in the chimney') and then out into the garden with the secateurs for half an hour, my infant daughter gathering aphids in my wake.

Still, the garden was waiting for me at the end of this train journey. The trip from Paddington to Stroud is a curious experience. From London to Swindon the terrain is fairly flat, with only a few mild Berkshire wolds and the odd Neolithic white horse cut in the chalk to divert the traveller.

At Swindon, however, you usually have to change trains, and plunge off down a long dark tunnel. It's a bit like Alice in Wonderland, especially when the train bursts out into daylight again and you find yourself looking down into a magic place: a deep, lush, solitary valley, its sides thickly wooded, and a handsome old Elizabethan manor house tucked away by a lake.

Then, a scatter of houses begins to appear on the opposite hillside, and a village emerges, every house odd and pretty and unique, perched on a steep hillside, their windows all flashing in the sun. When I am coming home from working in London this sight never fails to delight me: move me, even. Why can't modern houses be built like this: each one different, and all cuddling up together with a sense of shared history and of fun?

Framed by the hanging woods and the lush valley, how could anywhere be more perfect? Or indeed, more different from the endless leaden sprawl of London. Now, the sweetest moment of a day in London is the glimpse of this place from the train on the way home. The locals call it the Golden Valley: I, remembering the good Dr Johnson, prefer to think of it as the Happy Valley.

It is as if the eye blinks and for a split second sees

into another dimension, a queer little corner of Eden which has broken off and somehow survived, and where man lives with woman and with his neighbours and they call to each other across their garden walls, and the word work is never heard at all. They just live their lives on the steepest of sunny green slopes, and never once stumble or fall.

'Let's go for a walk!' I cried one day when the sun had broken through and was blazing away to make up for lost time. We put Beano into a new sort of sling: the backpack, a more comfortable way to carry bigger babies. Yes, she was bigger. Even the clinic admitted that.

'She's all right,' beamed our doctor, bouncing her on her knee. 'She's lovely. It's always the ones you worry about who turn out all right.' So the nightmare was officially over.

Even my memories of Gloucester Hospital had grown a little softer round the edges. I was grateful for the surgical skill which had released Beano from her prison and kept me alive to enjoy her. It must have been a bad night for them, the night she was born. The flap and panic and disorder had probably been due as much to undermanning from government cuts as human error.

I wouldn't say all the bitterness had evaporated from my soul, or ever would. But the sweet memories of Stroud Hospital, run entirely by women, softened my attitudes a lot. It confirmed my long-held belief in the superiority and humanity of the small-scale institution every time. A friendly, family feeling hung about Stroud Hospital. All the women I've ever met who'd had babies in the Maternity Hospital thought of it with a nostalgic smile.

'Let's go to the Happy Valley'. I was intent on pursuing my glimpse of a pastoral utopia. That inviting little village I had seen from the train proved to be even more idyllic at close quarters. The main

240

street runs along just above the stream on the valley floor, and is so narrow, cars have to crawl along at less than walking pace. The honeycomb of little old houses perched on the hillside above can only be reached by a series of zigzag paths: apparently donkeys carried goods up, an idea which added to the exotic feeling of the place.

Beyond, at the end of the village, we entered the Happy Valley itself, past a children's playground set in the greenest glade I had ever seen. The shade of William Blake seemed to be sitting on my shoulder as Beano sat on Van Dyke's. Blake's Songs of Innocence kept riddling through my brain and I realized for the first time their glowing power, their piercing love for the infant soul, and their fear of its enemies. Beano must play free in just such an echoing green as this.

'I would die for her,' Van Dyke had once said, and I looked around for something to protect her from: some spotted snake with double tongue. But there was nothing: only the trees and the broken light and the stillness.

The weather held, and next day we went to Painswick Beacon, a famous vantage point, overlooking several counties: the Severn plain with its orchards, settlements and arcs of glinting water; and beyond, the dark hills of Wales. It is not a hard climb: a road goes nearly all the way there. Many families walk up there on clear summer days, with the grandparents picking their way slowly and the toddlers tumbling among the rabbit holes. It is pleasant to be among such company, under the soft September sun.

At the top, we sat and stared at England slumbering below us on all sides, so far and blue and lovely. Sitting there, lifted up above the busy workaday world, so it was no more than a buried hum from below, with a few other families laughing nearby in the wind, I felt how ordinary it was, what had happened to me. What could be more ordinary than having a child? What was I making all the fuss about? And yet it did seem miraculous to me and, presumably, also to all the other parents who watched their children misbehaving cheerfully along the edge of the elegant and elevated Painswick Golf Course.

Below the golf-course turf lie, no doubt, Victorian pennies, heavy and black with age, Elizabethan buckles, fragments of Saxon pottery and Roman glass. And had an Ancient British baby sat here, ever, looking out over the heaving forest to where the big river ran? The same sun would have warmed her wispy head, the same delight might have danced in her mother's heart, for it felt like a very old dance to me. It seemed a good moment to have glimpsed this serenity. Tomorrow was my birthday. I was going to be forty.

Chapter 24

Actually, I wasn't forty. I was thirty-nine. When I realized this, I was quite disappointed. I wanted to be forty. I felt forty. Hell, I deserved forty. I suppose a lot of people who are forty don't even notice it. If you're anchored in a stable family, with elderly children, maybe: or living in the same place you've always lived, going through the usual soothing routines, forty might not seem like anything special.

Most people have their babies long before forty. Their youth is mixed with duty and by the time they're forty they might easily be grandparents. For me, though, youth had been youth, and had gone on as long as decently possible. But now it was over, and the flesh and the devil, my former favourites, had limped off, defeated, to their lairs. My fling was flung. My bright day was done, and Beano's was just dawning.

Now I must give myself up to the duties and responsibility. The prospect was surprisingly refreshing. First of all, I decided, I really must break my way out of the post-baby cocoon and find out what was going on in Stroud. I'd been vaguely aware of debates in the local paper about redevelopment schemes, but was too preoccupied to master the detail.

I went to see Joe Oregano, Winnie Windbreaker's Green man, in search of information. I found him still bearded, but with a new, short haircut. Not so much John the Baptist now as Sir Walter Raleigh. And as it happened, I found him poised to set sail, metaphorically speaking, into the choppy seas of local politics. He was going to stand as Green Party candidate in the local council elections.

This was obviously a good thing, I thought. Stroud was so full of gentle pleasures. It was, I felt, a democratic, relaxed little town that left you alone if you wanted to be alone, but smiled and had time for you if you had time for it. The blackbird, singing by the churchyard wall, had often charmed me, as had the old-fashioned drapers with their faintly genteel 1950s gloom. The—

'Of course, we've got the highest number of nuclear plants in the world round here,' Joe Oregano was saying.

'What?'

'Yes: Berkeley, Oldbury, and Hinckley. And the CEGB are planning three more.'

'Good God!'

'Yes. And all up and down the Severn there are higher-than-normal patterns of certain sorts of cancer and other diseases associated with radiation.' I felt sick.

'What about the countryside, though?' I wondered, clinging to my pastoral utopia as the cracks spread right across its face. 'I mean, it's so lovely round here, isn't it? It's all right, isn't it?

It was not. The Friends of the Earth organization had completed a survey of beech and yew trees in Gloucestershire and discovered that symptoms of acid rain damage were widespread. 62 per cent of beech trees and 76 per cent of yew trees were already affected. They concluded that damage in Britain is perhaps five or six years behind that on the continent of Europe. The rain, which I had thought so mild and sweet, part of the English scene, is apparently as acid nowadays as vinegar.

'What causes it?'

'It's the burning of fossil fuels. Mainly from power stations and cars' exhausts.' I felt sicker.

'But Stroud itself is being well cared for now, isn't it? This new development in the High Street, for instance. I've got the idea that it's rather a good thing, isn't it? Aren't they renovating all the old buildings? And ... isn't there going to be a wholefood restaurant?' I concluded lamely, as if a reliable supply of vegetarian lasagne would shore up the walls of paradise.

'Yes, the High Street development's OK, but the Union Street one is another matter.'

Stroud's small-scale, higgledy-piggledy charm was in danger, it seemed. There were apparently plans to bulldoze some of the quaint lanes and crooked corners and slap down a vast supermarket.

I saw red. Or rather, Green. My delusions of utopian bliss had been blown sky high. There wasn't just a serpent in this Eden: it was a seething pit of snakes. The peculiar charm of Stroud, which had stolen over my heart, must not be bulldozed away to make way for supermarkets. I wasn't against the new – but surely the new should be human scale, particular, and individual, or everywhere will end up just anywhere – as much of post-war Britain already is.

I strode angrily home up the hill, pausing only to have a mild heart attack outside Joe's Chippy when the gradient reached 1 in 5. I peered through the window. Where had Ralph Richardson gone? The original proprietor had resembled the great man not least in the lordly way he handled his chip-vat. Not so

245

much noble as regal. Had he, like the real Richardson, slipped off into the dark while my back was turned? O Mutabilitie. I was having plenty of thoughts, now, about the subject of *change*. It may have been too late for *Stop the Week* but it might not be quite too late to Stop the Rot.

I arrived home to find a birthday lunch in preparation. Good Lord! It was still my birthday. I felt that years had passed since I'd set off for town, serene and idyllic, confident that I'd found a place in which Beano could grow up protected from the worst of worldly wickedness. She waved her star-shaped hands at me and cried, 'Ma Ma!' I seized her with renewed passion now I knew what dangers awaited her.

The local paper was on the kitchen table and another terrifying word leapt out of it at me as I passed: meningitis. I'd been aware for months that the incidence of meningitis was much greater in Stroud than elsewhere in Britain. Nobody knows why. Now there were two more cases, one of them a baby exactly Beano's age, who lived just up the road and to whose mother I had chatted. About a month ago I'd read an agonizing article in THE *Guardian* by a woman whose baby had died within hours of contracting the disease.

She described waking up at 8 o'clock one morning and realizing that the baby wasn't babbling as usual, and going into her room and finding her locked rigid into her fever, fighting for her life. That image has haunted me ever since.

A few days later I'd woken up at 8.15, realized that Beano had not called us at 6.45 as usual, and gone hot and cold with fear and horror. I rushed into her room to find her snoring peacefully into her doll's ear. But the nightmare still lurks, and along with every other mother in Stroud, I think *It will be us next time*. I carried Beano out now, into the garden, trying to recover my spirits for my birthday lunch.

'Dar da!' she exclaimed. 'Teh dee! Ai-ee!'

'What does the sheep say?' I asked, needing to lose myself in small talk.

'Baaa! Baaa!'

'What does the cow say?'

'Erm-ooooooooooo!'

'What does the dog say?'

'Bwah! Bwah!'

But will there be any cows and sheep for her to see, I wondered, as I sang *Baa baa black sheep, have you any wool? Yes sir yes sir three bags full. One for my master and one for my dame. And one for the little boy who lives down the lane.*

My eye travelled across the opposite hillside where the sheep must so often have grazed, in this country where, in the past, the bags of wool had always been full. Would there be any lanes for Beano to roam in? Would there be any little boys? Would there be any Beano? I held my cheek against hers and shut my eyes while the world rocked.

The grandparents arrived, like the cavalry, to save the day, bearing home-made cake.

'Ba ba!' cried Beano – which meant, *Someone is coming.* She recognized her ancestors and gave them a devilish grin. She leaned out like a ship's figurehead, stretching her arms towards them.

It was warm enough to take her clothes off. She waved her white legs in the air. We ate under the plum tree which was heavy with fruit, and Beano explored the landscape of her grandfather's knee: the tickly tweed jacket, the strange bush of moustache. Hairy old history! She bounced on her launching pad: the grandparental knee. All around her the poisonous and poisoned trees stand and wait: to her they are only green.

That night it was my turn to put her to bed. She went to sleep with both hands up, as if in surprise. I sat beside her for a while, in the half-light from the drawn blind. Above our heads the mobiles twirled idly: the paper bees and sunflowers, the birds and frogs. My mournful old teddy bear leaned over and stared at his reflection in the mirror: tired and worn but still game. How many of my tears he had absorbed! And when my daughter's tears came, he would be ready with his kind eyes and soothing fur.

I glimpsed the shadow of an old woman in the glass, and then she dodged back and hid behind me. I felt my youth slipping away. We always dread its passing. *When I'm twenty-six*, the teenager warns, *I'll kill myself*. And for women it's particularly hard to encounter middle age: the time, we suspect, when the kissing has to stop. After all, people don't say, 'That's a wonderful old Georgian wife John's got, isn't it?' Objects appreciate as they age: mere women only dwindle. Then we are no good as sirens or baby-factories. It's no wonder we creep dolefully past forty, as if it's an afterlife with Abandon Hope written above the gate.

But what was happening, here and now? I hesitated under the gate, the dizzy parade of youth behind me, its rockets and rhythms beginning, now, to fade. But up ahead – astonishing! Instead of the blank wall I had feared, a new landscape was opening up. My daughter was leading me, paradoxically, around to the very beginning of things: backwards through the looking glass into a wonderland where dusty old memories stirred, unfurled themselves and gleamed gold-vermilion.

Was that a house among the red rocks? Or was it a doll's house? A wolf lurked deep in the woods, but his paws were velvet. A horse stared over a gate: a strange, painted stare. Stars hung above, and glittered, and turned: who hung them there? I saw a warm stone where we might sit and play. I heard an echoing shout in the meadow. I saw us glide out in a small boat upon the jade water. In the far distance, real horses, real wolves, real pitiless stars, all wait. But that is beyond another gate, and we can lock it for a moment while we swim, my ivory babe and I, in the jade water, and I realize: she gave birth to me.

Eventually I hauled myself to my feet. For a second the nursery world wheeled around me and the stars fizzed. That was another thing: I had to lose weight and get fit. The young lie in bed all day, and are as elastic as snakes. We oldies stand up and crack like dry old twigs. I tiptoed creakingly out of her room and back into the world of TV screens. Van Dyke was slumped in front of ours, swearing at the news.

'How are you getting on with your book?' he asked. I sighed heavily.

'Not very well. Everything I've written so far is all wrong. I'll have to start again.'

'Why don't you start again now: on your birthday?' I stood watching TV for a moment first. On the screen, somebody carried a baby into the picture. I knew by heart the soft rubbery feel of it. I knew it by muscle and skin.

'Isn't it odd?' I mused. 'A couple of years ago I was frightened of babies. Now whenever I see one I want to cuddle it.'

'Ah well,' observed Van Dyke. 'Perhaps at last you are turning into a human being.'

I went upstairs to my workroom. I had to make a new start with my work, too. I had to sail between so many worlds now. Like an Elizabethan adventurer, I had glimpsed new coasts, lost in the fogs, and an unknown land beyond which sent the earthy smell of fruit and fertility across the waves to me, with faint echoes of dangerous howls and menacing drums. I had to leap into the surf, crying out the name of my queen.

There was the nursery world to explore with my tiny captain – a world which, despite adults' attempts to make a pastoral escape out of it, is haunted none the less by the demon and the mask, the twitching curtain and the staring moon. Even babies have bad dreams, however fantastical their brick palaces spread out on the carpet in yellow and blue and green.

As for the real dull world of bills and rates and taxes: well, at the very moment when I'd thought I was settling gracefully into my middle years, and everything was getting gentler, with the roots going down, and the friendly warmth of provincial life creeping up, it turned out that even mild green Gloucestershire was a perilous place. Instead of drawing up my armchair to the fire, I had to put on my armour and go out and fight.

Because I was her knight. If the world was spoiled for my baby, what was the point of anything? Forty had not brought ripeness and relaxation, but a call to arms. For her and all the other babies, I had to struggle on in the tedious battlefield of pamphlets and campaigning. Goodness! I had ideals! It was like being young again.

Ideals need fresh air. I opened the window and looked out at the stars. It was the year when the comet passed close to the earth, but I could not see it. If Beano survived, she would be an old woman when it came flaring back to look at our planet again. What sort of world would it find? Would music rise from our islands and into the upper air? Or blank clouds hang on its silent and spoiled face? I had been prepared to turn a sceptical blind eye to all that, but now I had a child, I was torn between fury and hope. I had woken up and seen the earth fall into the hands of Homo Sapiens, that tinkering, greedy ape.

I turned on the baby intercom. Through it I could hear her snortling away in her sleep. It was bad enough not being able to protect her from the common cold, let alone radiation and acid rain and meningitis. And the featureless monotony of mass-production – that ingenious invention of Homo Sapiens. But she was a member of Homo Sapiens, too. And when we lifted her out of the bath, white light streamed off her, dazzling the ducks. For her I had to fight, to take it all on and, hardest of all, believe in the victory of angel over ape. Was this being human? At last?

She sighed down the baby intercom – but I could have heard it across deserts of vast eternity. She was roaming in the strange halls of sleep, while I, too, turned to an imagined world: the one the writer must struggle to shape, beginning again out of a void. I paused to listen to her breathe, her little life shivering like a candle in the black blast of fate: the comet outside the window and the invisible germ in the night stormed down at her, and what could we protect her with but our humanity and our hope? Some place their trust in divinities, but they are too capricious for me.

Although – as she lies in her cot, sometimes, she seems to be flying, arms outspread, hair blown back, eyes closed. I must trust her, launch her and let her go, and fall back broken in her slipstream. The hardest thing of all: the letting go. Ordinary mortal though she will certainly prove, there was a moment when I saw her flying thus by night: flying with her bow and arrows right round the spinning globe. The fatal thump of love: the only true god. She'd shot me through the heart, all right: blind as a baby, yet her aim was true. What else might she not achieve? I took out the first sheet of white, waiting paper, dimmed the light slightly, and picked up my pen.

The End

UP THE
GARDEN PATH

by Sue Limb

Izzy has problems . . . fat and spotty (too many cream cakes), she is hopelessly in love with Michael. Michael, unfortunately, is married to Louise – and intends to stay that way. Meanwhile Izzy has to contend with the assorted delights and terrors of 4C (that would have to be her class!), put up with being adored by Dick (the pottery teacher), and somehow cope with the maniacal, larger-than-life attentions of Hywel and Gwyn, two sex-mad Welshmen who force their way into her life and affections, in spite of their very obvious faults . . .

0552 12561X

CLASS
by Jilly Cooper

CLASS IS DEAD! OR so everyone claims. Who better to refute this than Jilly Cooper!

Describing herself as 'upper middle class', Jilly claims that snobbery is very much alive and thriving! Meet her hilarious characters! People like Harry Stow-Crat, Mr and Mrs Nouveau-Richards, Samantha and Gideon Upward, and Jen Teale and her husband Brian. Roar with laughter at her horribly unfair observations on their everyday pretensions – their sexual courtships, choice of furnishings, clothes, education, food, careers and ambitions ...

For they will all remind you of people that you know!

'Highly entertaining, acerbic and wickedly observant ... certain to become as much part of the verbal shorthand as was Nancy Mitford's *U and Non-U* a generation ago'
The Economist

'Enormously readable and very funny'
Cosmopolitan

0 552 11525 8

A SELECTED LIST OF TITLES
AVAILABLE FROM CORGI BOOKS

☐	10427 2	BELLA	Jilly Cooper	£2.99
☐	10277 6	EMILY	Jilly Cooper	£2.99
☐	10576 7	HARRIET	Jilly Cooper	£2.99
☐	11149 X	IMOGEN	Jilly Cooper	£2.99
☐	12041 3	LISA & CO	Jilly Cooper	£2.99
☐	10717 4	OCTAVIA	Jilly Cooper	£2.99
☐	10878 2	PRUDENCE	Jilly Cooper	£2.99
☐	12486 9	RIDERS	Jilly Cooper	£4.99
☐	13264 0	RIVALS	Jilly Cooper	£4.99
☐	11525 8	CLASS	Jilly Cooper	£3.99
☐	99208 9	THE 158lb MARRIAGE	John Irving	£4.99
☐	99204 6	THE CIDER HOUSE RULES	John Irving	£5.99
☐	99209 7	THE HOTEL NEW HAMPSHIRE	John Irving	£4.99
☐	99369 7	A PRAYER FOR OWEN MEANY	John Irving	£5.99
☐	99206 2	SETTING FREE THE BEARS	John Irving	£4.99
☐	99207 0	THE WATER METHOD MAN	John Irving	£4.99
☐	99205 4	THE WORLD ACCORDING TO GARP	John Irving	£4.99
☐	12865 1	LOVE FORTY	Sue Limb	£4.99
☐	12873 2	LOVE'S LABOURS	Sue Limb	£2.99
☐	12561 X	UP THE GARDEN PATH	Sue Limb	£3.50
☐	01298 8	THE WORDSMITHS OF GORSEMERE (Trade Paperback)	Sue Limb	£6.95
☐	99239 9	BABYCAKES	Armistead Maupin	£4.99
☐	99383 2	SIGNIFICANT OTHERS	Armistead Maupin	£4.99
☐	11554 1	TALES OF THE CITY	Armistead Maupin	£4.99
☐	99086 8	MORE TALES OF THE CITY	Armistead Maupin	£4.99
☐	99106 6	FURTHER TALES OF THE CITY	Armistead Maupin	£4.99